James Reaney's

Apple Butter & Other Plays for Children

published with assistance from the Canada Council

Talonbooks
201 1019 East Cordova
Vancouver 6
British Columbia
Canada

This book was typeset by Beverly Matsu, designed by Elizabeth Komisar with Beverly
Matsu, and printed by the Hunter Rose Company for Talonbooks.

First printing: December 1973

Talonplays are edited by Peter Hay.

Cover design and drawing by Sandra Barrett.

Rights to produce Apple Butter & Other Plays for Children, in whole or in part, in any
medium or by any group, amateur or professional, are retained by the author, and
interested persons are requested to apply for permission and for terms to his agent,
Sybil Hutchinson, Apt. 409, Ramsden Place, 50 Hillsboro Avenue, Toronto, Ontario,
M5R 1S8, who is authorized to negotiate.

ISBN 0-88922-043-3

Preface

These four plays are part of my life in the sixties and for a fuller explanation of this see an article in *Canadian Literature*, No. 41, called "Ten Years at Play." Originally I wanted to call this book *Schoolplays* — since the plays as I remember their productions swarm with schools, public, nursery, private and high. As you read them in the order suggested here with the marionette play first — you can watch somebody grow up. It happens to be true in this community that one or two children I know *did* see *Apple Butter* at the Western Fair in 1965 and did, a few years later, find themselves old enough to be in the last play — *Ignoramus*. In a way I've hoped to produce a work like Carl Orf's musical programme for children or the Kodaly method in which poetry, imagination, metaphors slowly become more and more as natural to you as breathing.

When I directed Listeners' Workshop these plays were basic to the Saturday morning sessions. Things developed around them — young directors, young and old playwrights. Given this book it is possible to develop a grassroots theatre movement based on classical and local traditions (*Ignoramus* depends on both Aristophanes and a CBC Citizens Forum broadcast). It was tantalizing to see all this just beginning when it had to stop through lack of funds, but I'm still amazed at how little money enters into it: there has to be some, but the basic need is root ideas that uncurl in a community until you find yourself taking a workshop to a school gym in the slums or helping 129 teachers in Niagra Falls (Autumn 1970) improvise a play using their local paper as the script and the costumes with sound effects from the city's spare drain pipes and bike wheels! Members of the old Listeners' Workshop ('67—'69) have been working still with the idea; Jo-Anne Cheung was just telling me on the front steps of the Library how she once took a neighbourhood group for a walk to see if they could hear how *different* their footsteps sounded on a certain stretch of sidewalk on Raymond Avenue.

I hope these plays will help you to *listen* as beautifully as this. Don't be afraid to make changes that fit in with your particular place. As a matter of fact it might be fun to take out the basic idea of each play and improvise your own play around it. Eventually you should be able to take a walk down the corridors of your apartment or the sidewalks of your neighbourhood and come back with a play you have played out and listened to on the way.

James Reaney
London, Ontario
May 31, 1971

Apple Butter

A Note for Apple Butter

This marionette play was commissioned for children attending the Western Fair, London, Ontario, in the fall of 1965. First performances were given in a tent on the fairgrounds. The local references can be changed to whatever suits the audience. Moo Cow, for example, could have a map of Vancouver Island on her first side. To work the characterization well, probably each actor should actually make the marionette he is manipulating and "speaking". The relationship between marionette and actor is something like that between doll and little girl, Teddy Bear and Christopher Robin. The audience, of course, will show you how this works: after a performance in Woodstock, Ontario, children practically accompanied Apple Butter right to the station; and in the tent at the Fair babies who cried through everything else shut up for Moo Cow, while backstage visitors enquired after Rawbone with a great deal of respect. Pace and rhythm can be adjusted to the "feel" of the audience for the various marionettes; the kind of "Wuzzle" reaction you get will tell you where you're at with the audience, but long before that you'll know and can start adjusting.

The original production opened in Western Fair week, September 1965, with the following: Theatre Construction — Eric Bremner, Stage facade — John Chambers, Moo Cow designed by Jay Peterson, Roles and Manipulation by John and Gillian Ferns, Ellen Richardson and the author, assisted by Alvin Wagner, Chris Faulkner and Jill Bradnock. Set designed by James Anderson.

CHARACTERS

HESTER PINCH   an old maid

SOLOMON SPOILROD   a schoolmaster

VICTOR NIPCHOPPER   thick skulled, overalls, rubber boots

APPLE BUTTER   made of apple wood, peg nose, auger
                                       drilled eyes, raffia hair

TREEWUZZEL   a tree fairy made of old pieces of wood
                                       picked up in the bush; attach fresh leaves
                                       for each performance

MOO COW   flat, wooden, white with a black map of
                                       Canada on one side suggesting Holstein
                                       markings

RAWBONE   a bone fairy, made out of cattle bones;
                                       thigh bone for face and torso, smaller
                                       bones for arms and legs. Use a drill for
                                       simple hole eyes and mouth

Scene: The yard of Miss Pinch's farmhouse in southwestern Ontario, about 1890. Her house has a gable with a pointed window; an elm tree almost screens a watering trough and a large bank barn.

When the curtain goes up, we see MISS PINCH, SPOILROD, NIPCHOPPER and APPLE BUTTER line up onstage ready to be introduced by a voice which says:

A farmhouse in southern Ontario about 1890. The farmhouse is owned by a spinster, Miss Hester Pinch. She has a hired man who works the farm for her called Victor Nipchopper. She boards the schoolmaster, Solomon Spoilrod. Miss Pinch has lately adopted an orphan called Apple Butter. When the curtain goes up we find Mr. Spoilrod and Miss Pinch discussing this orphan.

NIPCHOPPER and APPLE BUTTER now go off, leaving MISS PINCH with SOLOMON SPOILROD.

PINCH:

Well, Solomon Spoilrod, you look as if you put in a hard day's work teaching school to-day!

SOLOMON:

I guess I do look somewhat fatigued, Miss Pinch.

PINCH:

My first name's Hester, Solomon. You're late home from school. Usually you're home here at half-past four, but to-day — why it must be five to five!

SOLOMON:

It would have been later but the switch broke.

PINCH:

The switch broke?

SOLOMON:

Yes, Hester, I had to beat all the school children to-day, they were so naughty. I had just got nicely warmed up when that Smith boy deliberately broke my best birch rod with his back. And, of course, I'd never strike a child with my bare hand.

PINCH:

For land sakes, Solomon, what did all your scholars do that was so naughty?

SOLOMON:

They rubbed off the list of names I put on the blackboard yesterday of those that confessed to rubbing off the list of names of culprits I'd put up on the blackboard the day before.

PINCH:

Did they all — all forty-three children — rub off the names?

SOLOMON:

No. But none of them would say who had. So I had to whip them all. Spare the child and spoil the rod, you know, Hester.

PINCH:

Oh Solomon — don't you mean it the other way round?

SOLOMON: *gives a dry little rusty laugh*

Yes, Hester, I suppose I do. Which reminds me. How is that new orphan you're adopting from the orphanage doing? Has your hired man been able to get much work out of him lately? Or does the young orphan lad need some corrective

12

encouragement?

PINCH:

    Solomon, this is the strangest orphan the orphanage has ever sent me.

SOLOMON:

    How — the strangest, Hester?

PINCH:

    First of all, he's very small and yet at other times he looks very big. His hair's so long, sometimes I think maybe it's a girl they've sent me.

SOLOMON:

    What's this remarkable creature's name?

PINCH:

    Well, I can hardly say that either. It — calls itself Apple Butter. Surely its first name must be Paul. Paul Butter. Who ever heard of even an orphan called Apple Butter!

Enter APPLE BUTTER.

APPLE BUTTER:

    Yep. That's my name all right, Miss Pinch. First name — Apple. Second name — Butter. I guess it's my sweet disposition. The steward and the matron at the orphanage said I was just like all the apples in the orchard rolled into one barrel — all the russet apples, spy apples and Mackintosh apples — all squashed together into a sweet sticky brown mess people put in crocks and call APPLE BUTTER.

PINCH:

    Apple Butter, this here is the schoolmaster, Mr. Solomon Spoilrod.

APPLE BUTTER:

    How do you do, Mr. Spoilrod. The school kids were telling me what a kind hearted father you are to them all. Why, you purposely use the softest hickory stick you can find!

SOLOMON:

    Hah! Rusty ought to be your real name, Apple Butter. You're plumb full of ancient irony. Now, look here. None of your apple sauce with Miss Pinch, here. Aren't you a lucky lad being adopted by her into a nice healthy farm like this?

APPLE BUTTER:

    Oh — I suppose.

SOLOMON:

You suppose! I hope she got a good apple when she got you. Let's test your physical fitness. Lift your right arm! Your left! Your left leg! Your right leg! Lie down! Stamp your foot.

As APPLE BUTTER does all these things, sometimes hesi-tantly, sometimes not — we get a chance to know what he is like as a marionette.

Well, Hester, it looks as if you might get some work out of him.

PINCH:

Oh, he's a sturdy little fellow.

SOLOMON:

Now, Apple Butter, let's test your mental ability. What weighs more — a pound of iron, or a pound of feathers?

APPLE BUTTER: *pause*

They both weigh the same! Which would you rather I threw at you?

SOLOMON:

I'm not sure. If the feathers were rolled up tight enough they could present you with quite a buffet.

˙APPLE BUTTER:

It bears thinking on, don't it, Master Spoilrod?

We hear wind sighing through tree branches which sway slightly.

That's a great lovely tree you have in front of your house, Miss Pinch.

PINCH:

It's a grand old tree. But I've told my hired man, Victor Nipchopper, to cut it down. We're right out of firewood.

APPLE BUTTER:

No need to cut such a fine old tree down, ma'am. There's a big dead old tree down by the river that the storm must have blown down last night. It's practically cut up into firewood already.

Enter the HIRED MAN with axe.

14

VICTOR:

Yuh want this tree chopped down, Miss Pinch? I figure I just got time to chop it down before supper. There's nothing I like better than chopping down a tree!

APPLE BUTTER: *after a pause*

It doesn't look as if it wanted to be chopped down.

PINCH:

Why no, Victor Nipchopper. Apple Butter, or Paul Butter, or whatever this orphan lad's name is, says there's a big dead tree all fallen over by the river we could use for firewood.

VICTOR: *aside to APPLE BUTTER*

Why'd you have to tell her about that dead tree! I like chopping down live trees; besides, I figured on selling off the wood from that dead tree for kindling. Well, I feel like getting back at you, Butter!

APPLE BUTTER:

That's natural. When you rub fur the wrong way there should be some sparks.

VICTOR:

Hester Pinch, give this orphan kid a licking. He didn't do the job he was supposed to do at all, all the saft.

PINCH:

Paul Butter, I'm amazed to hear you've been shirking your chores. Victor Nip-chopper what *was* this orphan child's task about the farm this afternoon?

VICTOR:

He was supposed to see that the crows didn't fly down and eat up the newly planted corn. He was told to watch the crows.

APPLE BUTTER:

That's what I did. I watched the crows.

PINCH:

Land of Goshen, child, you're supposed to do more than that.

APPLE BUTTER:

So I learn now. Nobody told me I was to keep them from doing something. Turnip Chopper here just said "Watch the crows," so I watched them.

PINCH:

When they fly down you're supposed to shout at them, throw a stick at 'em, shoot'em.

The marionette "takes" the stage with the gestures these words suggest.

APPLE BUTTER:

Yes, Miss Pinch. But how can I shoot crows without a gun?

VICTOR:

Don't give him a gun, Hester Pinch, or our days are numbered. By the way, what did you call me a little while back?

APPLE BUTTER:

Why I believe I pronounced your last name as Turnip Chopper. Isn't your real name Vic Turnipchopper?

VICTOR:

My name, you smart aleck, is *first name,* Victor, and *second name* Nipchopper.

APPLE BUTTER:

Well, it bears thinking on.

PINCH:

It bears more than thinking on, child. Apple Butter, if you let the crows eat up all the newly planted corn and it five shin plasters a bushel, you'll have to be punished.

APPLE BUTTER:

But I watched the crows. You're lucky I did even that. At first I thought he said, "Go over and wash the clothes." I walked all over the field looking for clothes, but all I could find was the scarecrow's.

SOLOMON:

I'll punish him for you, Hester.

VICTOR:

Let me give him a licking. I like to punish lazy orphan kids.

PINCH:

You men are just brutes. No, Apple Butter will punish himself. Do you want your supper, Butter?

APPLE BUTTER:

Do I want my supper! Does Butter want his supper!

16

PINCH:

    Then you'll have to have a whipping.

APPLE BUTTER:

    Strange meal-ticket that. "Little Apple Butter/ Gets whipped for his supper."
    That's not the way the song goes.

PINCH:

    Then — Apple Butter — off you go and select the stick you want me to beat you
    with.

APPLE BUTTER:

    I have to pick out my own switch, eh. Sounds like fun. Can it be just the stick I
    choose?

PINCH:

    A suitable switch, Apple Butter. Then I'll beat you with it and after this you'll
    watch the crows properly.

APPLE BUTTER:

    Suitable, eh. It bears thinking on. Suitable. Suitable. A suitable switch to beat me with.

    Exit APPLE BUTTER.

SOLOMON:

    You're far too soft on him, Hester.

VICTOR:

    There's an old log over there, Hester Pinch. I could beat him with that.

PINCH:

    Never mind. You men lack the woman's touch. By the way, now I have both of
    you here. Victor Nipchopper, isn't it true that after we finished our game of three-
    handed King Pedro last night and four glasses of my chokecherry wine, isn't it true
    that Spoilrod here proposed marriage to me and that I accepted him? This morning
    over his porridge he claims that he can't remember any such thing.

VICTOR:

    Well, Hester Pinch, I'll try to remember. At the second glass of chokecherry wine.....

    Enter APPLE BUTTER with a small chip in his hand.

APPLE BUTTER:

    Miss Pinch, does this look like a suitable stick to beat me with?

PINCH:

Why — it's nothing but a teeny-weeny chip of wood. I need eagle-eyed spectacles to even see the dratted thing!

APPLE BUTTER:

It may not be very big, but it certainly weighs heavy. Just look at the way it drags down my arm.

PINCH:

Now look here, Master Butter. Do you yourself feel that that minute little chip of wood is a suitable switch to punish a child with?

APPLE BUTTER:

Hmhm. You see I tested it out.

PINCH:

On what? Your own bottom, I suppose.

APPLE BUTTER:

No. I tested it out on an ant. It sure did make that ant feel sorry for stealing that ear of wheat from the granary.

PINCH:

But you're not an ant.

APPLE BUTTER:

No, but I've a married brother, Apple Cider, with kids — so I'm an uncle.

PINCH:

Back you go, child, before I lose my temper, and find me a suitable stick to beat you with. These men here are saying I'm spoiling you.

APPLE BUTTER: *exit*

Suitable, suitable. It bears thinking on, and when I think it appears that what she means is something suitable and larger.

PINCH:

Now. You were saying, Victor Nipchopper, that at the second glass of chokecherry wine Solomon Spoilrod here said.....

SOLOMON:

I'm sure it was the chokecherry wine, Hester.

18

PINCH:

What on earth do you mean? It wasn't my looks, it was the excitement of winning at King Pedro, eh? First of all, my chokecherry wine is temperance and second of all, I was very bad at King Pedro last night. Solomon Spoilrod, are you, or are you not, going to marry me? I've got a witness here.....

A mysterious sound offstage — a musical or tooting sound.

SOLOMON:

I think I'll go back to the school. I just remembered having locked one of the Junior Thirders in the woodbox.

VICTOR:

Give me ten dollars and I'll say I slept all through the third game, Spoilrod.

PINCH:

Oh, for pity sakes! What kind of switch is the child bringing me now!

Enter APPLE BUTTER with quite a large flowering bush in his hand.

SOLOMON:

Well, Hester, it *is* larger.

PINCH:

Butterkin, you've just pulled up my best spiraea bush.

APPLE BUTTER:

But, Miss Pinch — or Mother — or whatever you want me to call you. You did hint you wanted something you can see, and you can see this, can't you? And if you hit me with it, it certainly should hurt me. I hit the woodshed with it and it's half fallen over.

PINCH: *screams*

I can't even lift it. You've tricked me, Apple Butter, this time. But you watch out. I'm going out to cut down a stick to beat you with — and it'll be just small enough for my hand, and just big enough for your behind. *Exit PINCH.*

Show the audience "real" versions of the proposed switches as they are mentioned — birch and thorn and maple.

SOLOMON:

Whew! Thank Heavens she's got off the marriage proposal obsession. Ah, I think I can find some good stout switches in my favourite birch grove. *Exit.*

VICTOR:

And I'll find a cane from that old thorn tree down the lane.   *Exit.*

APPLE BUTTER: *alone*

What shall I, will I, do! They'll all be back in a minute with canes, rods, switches, ferules, and birches. All directed at me and my —

A whole fan of switches can appear behind him, from above.

poor little back. Where shall I, will I, hide? Somebody help me!

Enter the TREE FAIRY, huge, twiggy and trailing leaves.

TREE WUZZEL:

Don't be afraid, Apple Butter. I have appeared to help you. I am the Tree Wuzzel.

APPLE BUTTER:

Tree Wuzzel. This bears thinking on. Tree Wuzzel.

TREE WUZZEL:

Indeed it does. We Wuzzels rule the world, each wuzzel to a separate kingdom — animal, vegetable, mineral, bone, paper. All the trees, all wooden things are ruled by me and must do as I say.

When you hear the trees sigh in the wind, their millions of leaves rustling and whispering,

Use wind and rattle sounds here.

it is my voice you hear.

When the branch taps at the windowpane late at night and seems to say — I want to come in — it is my hand that is knocking. When you are walking through the bush on a dark fall night —

APPLE BUTTER:

Something I very seldom do.

TREE WUZZEL:

Through the forest on a dark fall night and you hear the boughs scrape and scratch and squeak against each other high up in the darkness — it is I playing my violin — playing my tree-branch fiddle. I am the wuzzel of all wooden things. Do you be-believe me, Apple Butter?

APPLE BUTTER:

Do I believe you? How can I help it when you stand towering right over me!
Kneeling.   Not only do I believe you're the wuzzel of all wooden things, you're the wuzzel of the whole wide world.

TREE WUZZEL:

No, Apple Butter. Don't carry things too far. Now if you believe in me I can help you.

APPLE BUTTER:

That bears — yes, just how can you help me who am about to be belaboured by three cruel human beings with a thorn stick, a birch rod, and a maple switch in their three respective hands?

TREE WUZZEL:

Suppose you tell *me*.

APPLE BUTTER:

Why I guess, Wuzzel, you sure could frighten the daylights out of them and I'll go in and eat up their supper.

TREE WUZZEL:

I'm subtler than that, Master Butter. If they try to hit you with anything made of wood — simply say "Wuzzel" — and the wooden thing will hit them. What's the magic word?

APPLE BUTTER: *pause*
Wuzzel?

TREE WUZZEL:

Now, I'll hide back here just to see that everything goes as planned.

APPLE BUTTER:

There's just one thing, Tree Wuzzel. What if they try to hit me with something other than something wooden?

TREE WUZZEL:

That bears thinking on, as you so often say, Apple Butter.

APPLE BUTTER:

And another thing, Tree Wuzzel. Why are you helping me like this?

TREE WUZZEL:

Why you saved this old tree from being cut down for firewood, don't you remember?

It's one of my favourite whistling, rustling, and fiddling places — so, right there and then, I decided to help you. Besides, I'm tired of people using my kingdom of wood to beat children with. Apple Butter — take care. Here comes — Miss Pinch. *Exit.*

PINCH: *entering with a small switch*
All right, Paul Butter. Just let's get this punishment business over. Remember — this is going to hurt me about as much as it's going to hurt you.

APPLE BUTTER:
That bears thinking upon.

PINCH:
What did you say?

APPLE BUTTER:
Wuzzel!

PINCH:
Wuzzel! Is that all you have to say for yourself! Well, I'll wuzzel you, Apple Butter.

Screams as a huge wooden spoon comes in and beats her off the stage.

APPLE BUTTER:
Switch made of maple
Wooden spoon made of maple
To switch me, Miss Pinch, you won't be able!

TREE WUZZEL:
Keep up the good work, Apple Butter.

Enter SOLOMON with a formidable birch rod.

SOLOMON:
Very well, you nasty brat. You may be able to score off Hester Pinch. But you'll have more trouble getting rid of Solomon Spoilrod. My arms are strong. I've thrashed a thousand kids in my time. And you'll be.....

APPLE BUTTER:
Wuzzel!

SOLOMON:
Wuzzel! I'll wuzzel you, you young puppy!

22

A great wooden spoon beats him off.

TREE WUZZEL:

Keep up the good work, Apple Butter.

Enter VICTOR NIPCHOPPER with a great club.

VICTOR:

Yah! You buttery rascal — you're going to get pounded.

APPLE BUTTER:

Two down and one to go. But I've forgotten the magic word. What's the magic word!

Members of the audience can supply it to him. They are in control of the action for a few moments.

VICTOR:

Two down and one to go, eh? I'll fix your clock for you!

APPLE BUTTER:

Wuzzel!

A really gigantic wooden spoon demolishes the HIRED MAN.

Well, that was a hard day's work. I feel rather hungry. I think Miss Pinch has baked some strawberry pies for supper as well as other goodies. Perhaps I'll go in now and have a bite to eat. Get things sort of ready for the others, too, when they come back all tired and hungry from being chased around the country by my three wooden spoons.

Screams and beating sounds off stage.

Enter the COW.

Hello, Moo, How are you?

MOO COW:

Oh, Apple Butter. I need help this moment.

APPLE BUTTER:

Why, what's the matter, Moo Cow?

MOO COW:

I've got to be back at the Sharpwhistle Farm in ten minutes or I'll be sold to Schneider's Meat Packing Plant.

APPLE BUTTER:

Do you want me to carry you?

MOO COW:

No. It's just if I go round by the road I'll be caught, but if you open that gate for me I can run across the cornfield, jump over the line fence and pretend I was in the pasture all day long.

APPLE BUTTER:

Follow me, Moo Cow. Why have you been gallivanting all day up and down the back roads, you silly cow?

MOO COW:

I've been looking for my sister, my twin sister Tilly, who mysteriously disappeared yesterday.

APPLE BUTTER:

Do you think you'll ever find her?

MOO COW:

No. Poor Tilly. At first I thought she'd jumped over the fence and was wandering the roads. But now — I'm afraid she's been made into a bottle of Bovril or a Gladstone bag.

APPLE BUTTER:

Aw, I'm awful sorry to hear that, Moo. It doesn't bear thinking on.

MOO COW:

Apple Butter, being a cow is not being long. We generally end up struck by lightning under a tree during a thunderstorm. They flay off our hides and deposit the rest of us in a fence corner somewhere, somewhere the crows come to pick our bones. We just end up a heap of bones.

APPLE BUTTER:

Ow!

MOO COW:

But bones can be kind to you, Apple Butter, if you'll let me through the gate.

24

APPLE BUTTER:

Of course I will, Moo Cow. Say, you've got a map on the side of you!

MOO COW:

It's a map of the county where I was born, and my mother.

(In this case, Perth County, which the original audience was asked to identify.)

APPLE BUTTER:

And what have you got on the other side?

MOO COW:

A map of Canada.

Pause here to see if the children can spot this.

APPLE BUTTER:

Why?

MOO COW:

It's where my father was born. Somewhere. He was a roving beast.

APPLE BUTTER:

Wuzzel!

(If you have a prop gate this can be a mysterious moment.)

MOO COW:

Moo! That gate just opened by itself!

APPLE BUTTER:

You'd better hurry, Moo. I hear them calling you.

Cries of "Coboss!" are heard off stage.

Now I'll go in to my supper. *Exit APPLE BUTTER.*

The Three Adults now creep back, racked with groans.

PINCH:

There he is. That dratted orphan inside there. Eating up my strawberry pies!

SOLOMON:

We don't seem to have any luck trying to attack him with anything made of wood.

VICTOR:

I know. I just tried to throw a whippletree at him and it came back to hit me in the head.

PINCH:

Serves you right for trying to throw it through one of my windows. Do you know, you numbskulls, if we can't get him and spank him with a wooden switch — I've heard that in the city when a mother gets angry at her child she takes a hairbrush and lets it have it. Now my hairbrush happens to be of wood — but in the store down in the village they've just got in a shipment of whalebone hairbrushes. Let's go down and get three.

SOLOMON:

I'll buy a whole gross.

VICTOR:

Wait till he feels that bone on his behind. I'll buy two hairbrushes. *They exit.*

Enter the BONE FAIRY — literally made of bones.

APPLE BUTTER:

The stars are coming out. The dew begins to fall. I wonder what my friends are up to..... Hello, old stranger. Do you often walk here in the twilight shadows?

RAWBONE:

Apple Butter, you'll be glad to know that Moo Cow got home safely and her hookey from Sharpwhistle pasture will never be detected.

APPLE BUTTER:

That I'm glad to hear. But who are you? Another Wuzzel?

RAWBONE:

I am the spirit of all things bony.

APPLE BUTTER:

My bony lies over the ocean?

RAWBONE:

Call me Rawbone.

APPLE BUTTER:

Oooh. Rawbone it is.

RAWBONE:

Tree Wuzzel told me to come and help you.

APPLE BUTTER:

Bony Prince Charlie.

RAWBONE:

Apple Butter, that'll be enough of that sort of joke, if you don't mind. You are about to be attacked with things bony. I can help you. You helped my friend Moo Cow. I am the spirit of her ancestors. When you need my help, simply cry Rawbone!

APPLE BUTTER:

Like this. Rawbone!

RAWBONE:

Right. Now — you'd better hide in the house. It'll make it more difficult for them to beat you because they'll be afraid to break the windows.

APPLE BUTTER:

Into the house I go, then.

Both hide. Enter Three Adults with hairbrushes.

PINCH:

He's inside the house. I want him outside so I can get elbow room with this hairbrush. I'm liable to hit the suspended lamps if I spank him indoors.

SOLOMON:

How'll we get him to come outside? To tell the truth, I'm rather afraid to go in after him. Your house is so full of wooden things.....

VICTOR:

Including your head.

SOLOMON:

.....that all he has to do is say "Wuzzel" and I'm done for.

VICTOR:

Let's trick him into coming outside to us. How about that famous cow he's so fond of, Moo Cow up at the Sharpwhistle Farm. You other two clear off and I'll pretend to be Moo Cow in trouble.   *PINCH and SOLOMON exit.*   Moooooh!

APPLE BUTTER: *off stage*
    Is that you in trouble again, Moo Cow?

VICTOR:
    Moooooh! Come quickly, Apple Butter. I've broken my neck, I think, getting caught in this rail fence, and my tail's caught in the barbed wire. Moooooh!

APPLE BUTTER:
    Oh — Moo Cow. Wherever are you? I can't see you in the twilight.

VICTOR:
    Ahah! Caught you!

PINCH: *entering with SOLOMON*
    Now, Apple Butter, you've been a very naughty boy and you're going to get it.

SOLOMON:
    Get it is not quite the word for it, Butter.

APPLE BUTTER:
    Oh dear — this bears thinking on.

VICTOR:
    It certainly does, kid.

APPLE BUTTER:
    You three think you're going to spank me with those whalebone hairbrushes you got in your hands, eh?

ALL THREE:
    Yes!

APPLE BUTTER:
    Well, let's just put it this way. I, Apple Butter, beg of you not to try.   *He kneels.* Miss Pinch, I implore you.   *Prostrates himself.*   Nipchopper, I'll never get your name wrong again. Spoilrod, I may even help you keep the school children in better order — if only you won't try to spank me with those whalebone hairbrushes.

VICTOR:
    Uh. He's really scared now, folks. We'll teach you to watch the crows properly.

PINCH:
    Always remember, Apple Butter. This is going to hurt us *more* than it hurts you.

APPLE BUTTER:

These are words to think upon, Miss Pinch. Rawbone!

A huge whalebone brush enters and chases them about. MOO
COW enters and bears VICTOR off on her horns, saying:

MOO COW:

The very idea of you pretending to be me, Victor Nipchopper. I never caught my tail in a fence in my life. For I always jump over them neat and clean just the way I'm going to jump with you — over the moon.

She and VICTOR disappear up. SOLOMON and PINCH
kneel for mercy in front of APPLE BUTTER.

PINCH:

Forgive us, Apple Butter. We'll never try to spank you, or any other orphan child again.

APPLE BUTTER:

What about you, Solomon Spoilrod? Are you going to be so unmerciful to your scholars ever again?

SOLOMON:

No. Just don't let that Giant Hairbrush at me again.

APPLE BUTTER:

Now you know what it feels like to get birched and strapped, don't you.

SOLOMON:

Yes.

APPLE BUTTER:

It bears thinking upon, doesn't it. Now — another thing. Are you going to marry Miss Pinch here, like you keep promising to do every time you get tiddly on her chokecherry wine and mysteriously win all the games of King Pedro?

SOLOMON: *pause*

No!

APPLE BUTTER:

Wuzzel!

Either TREE WUZZEL appears or the Tree falls down on
SOLOMON.

SOLOMON:

Yes! If I say yes will he stop frightening me?

PINCH:

Oh Solomon, I never knew you really cared that much. Apple Butter, you aren't going to leave us now. Why, we'll adopt you as our first child and we'll will the farm to you, come what may. I don't know how I could be so cruel to such a wise, innocent child.

APPLE BUTTER:

Thank you very much, Miss Pinch. But now that the apples are getting ripe, I think I'd better walk around and look at all the orchards to help the people that own them make their apple butter and apple cider.

PINCH:

Where will you sleep? Back at the orphanage?

APPLE BUTTER:

No. I only stayed there for a while to help out. I like sleeping out best — under a wild apple tree. Goodbye, folks, and maybe I'll come to see you in the spring when the apple-blossoms are out and bring you a blossom baby.

PINCH AND SOLOMON:

Goodbye, Apple Butter. We can just feel how you've changed us.

SOLOMON:

I feel sweeter inside. And more loving.

PINCH:

I don't feel like Miss Pinch anymore. I feel like Mrs. Spoilrod.

The TREE WUZZEL and RAWBONE appear.

APPLE BUTTER:

How far will you walk with me, Tree Wuzzel and Rawbone?

TREE WUZZEL AND RAWBONE:

As far as you're going, Apple Butter.

APPLE BUTTER:

As far as I'm going..... That bears thinking on.

30

Geography Match

A Note for Geography Match

Geography Match was originally conceived as a play for Canada's Centennial, without child actors *necessarily* since their having to be at school would prevent touring. This fell through, and the first production was acted completely by school children. I've included the original programme in its entirety in order to show those interested in production just how much organization and detail the play demanded and generously received. There are many opportunities for participation on the part of the young actors who often come up with better ideas than the author or director; many sequences can be rehearsed separately with student directors and then sewn together at the last rehearsals. Again, the pace is vital; don't get lost in the detail. I suggest a prelude in which all the actors sit on the edge of the stage with the musical instrument of their choice, be it gazoo or transistor, and improvise a few solo bars from everybody. Since there should be a drummer for the whole production, preferably on stage, perhaps he can hold this overture together. At the opening night we had recorders, bass viols, piano, transistor, drum — a rainbow of sound, sometimes sounding together at prepared climaxes — very strangely! A further suggestion: have a break after the Carnival. This is a shamelessly patriotic play and should be played recklessly and with all stops pulled out!

The play covers a 30-day transit of Canada. Why not a calendar device that says e.g. 28 days left, 27, etc.

SUGGESTIONS FOR ROLE DUPLICATION

The play is written for two ingenue leads, two character leads supported by eight young actors:

Ingenue Lead   Headmaster, Tecumseh, Nanabozho

Ingenue Lead   Headmistress, the Iceberg Lady, the Nun, Jenny's Ma

Character Actor   Wolfwind, Grizzly Bear, Master of Ceremonies, Hairy Mammoth

Character Actress   Weathergood, Coyote, Muskeg Mag

Transy can play the Newsboy

Geography Match was first performed by Broughdale Public School at Middlesex College Theatre on May 19th, 1967, with the following cast:

Mistress of Ceremonies	Sylvia Frank
Newsboy	Steven Keene
Headmaster Stuffy-Smith	Paul Potter
Headmistress Birdwhistell	Karen Henkel
Mr. Wolfwind (Grizzly Bear)	Brian Millson
Miss Weathergood (Coyote)	Megan Thompson
The Iceberg Lady	Deirdre Wilson
The Nun	Susan Kennedy
Bonhomme de Neige	Ricky Biggs
Hairy Mammoth	Carol Keller
Jenny's Ma	Patricia Barry
Tecumseh	Paul Potter
Nanabozoho	Brian Millson
Muskeg Mag	Carol Keller
Simon Fraser	Paul Potter

Continuation School Kids		Academy Kids	
Jenny	Cathy Isaacs	Bullseye	David Stacey
Lunette	Kate Collie	Squeak Squeak	Scott Davidson
Jim	Bruce Jeffrey	Piper	Ricky Biggs
Transy	Andrew Gunn	Blubber Boy	Allan Rumbold

Music:

Shady Hill Theme	written by Paul Potter
Nothing Ever Happened Here	music played by Kate Collie
Minuet	played by Scott Davidson (flute) and Paul Potter (piano)

Backstage:

Costumes	Kate Collie, Megan Thompson, Jo-Anne Brash
Props	Sylvia Frank, Karen Henkel
Sound Effects	David Stacey and Steven Keene (on drums)
Stage Manager	Paul Hooker
Lighting	Paul Potter and Dale Brown
Make-up	Sylvia Frank and Susan Kennedy
Tickets and Publicity	Susan Kennedy, Cathy Isaacs, Sylvia Frank, Paul Potter and James Reaney.

Directed by James Reaney
Codirected by Noelle Jack and Sylvia Frank

CHARACTERS

MASTER OF CEREMONIES

NEWSBOY

HEADMASTER STUFFY-SMITH

HEADMISTRESS BIRDWHISTELL

MR.WOLFWIND: GRIZZLY BEAR

MISS WEATHERGOOD: COYOTE

THE ICEBERG LADY

THE NUN

BONHOMME DE NEIGE *mute or papier-mache figure*

HAIRY MAMMOTH

JENNY'S MA

TECUMSEH

NANABOZHO

MUSKEG MAG

CONTINUATION SCHOOL KIDS:	ACADEMY KIDS:
JENNY	BULLSEYE
LUNETTE	SQUEAK SQUEAK
JIM	PIPER
TRANSY	BLUBBER BOY

ACADEMY KIDS

BULLSEYE: Aggressive and barrel-chested

BOY WITH PIPE: A long stemmed clay pipe such as they used to smoke in Old Chum tobacco calendars. Fair and elegant. His nickname is "Piper" and he carries a guitar slung over his back.

SQUEAK SQUEAK: Keeps a pet white mouse. Red hair, really classless, a zoology-biology buff.

BLUBBER BOY: Like Arthur in *Tom Brown's School Days;* parents off in Florida, lonely and sensitive and small

CONTINUATION SCHOOL KIDS

JENNY: The big tomboy type, sweater type, sweater and skirt completely unsophisticated and probably only at school because she has to be. Sometimes plays a mouth-organ.

LUNETTE: A tall thin, very clever girl with glasses and dressed in a good sweater coat. She is Jenny's Don Quixote. Her head is always in a book or she is practising her recorder.

JIM: A medium-sized boy — plain and even-tempered. Like a cowboy whittling or a sailor scrimshawing, he has always to be doing something with his hands. The spool knitting is probably part of something he is making for his mother.

TRANSY: A small wiry shrewd tricky boy completely devoted to his transistor radio. He is quite capable of betraying the whole group for the sake of the radio. He should be portrayed as under the influence of the Liverpool Sound of the early and mid-Sixties. He should have a huge collection of something like bubble gum cards, with pictures of rock and roll singers on them.

As for the schoolmaster and schoolmistress: STUFFY-SMITH in round glasses and boyish smile; slender and occasionally sings things under his breath to himself. MISS BIRDWHIS-tell ideally should be (no glasses) the Anne of Green Gables type — rather Irish looking. Anglican vs United Church.

MASTER OF CEREMONIES: *children with flags and a staircase*
  Ladies and gentlemen, the children of the nations show their basic physical fitness
  by — THE STAIR TEST! The Norwegian child — can still climb a pair of stairs!
  The English child — can still climb a pair of stairs. Oops, the American child's test
  will have to be delayed. He's just fainted. Now instead we'll have that rugged cub
  of the Northern Wilds — the Canadian child — try his basic world stair-climbing test.

  The Canuck child dissolves halfway up and collapses.

  Uh — well, folks — give the cub of the Northern Wilds a big hand anyhow. That was
  a noble try of sorts, Little Johnny Beaver Canuck.

NEWSBOY: *runs down aisle*
  Read all about it. Duke of Edinburgh blasts Canadian tots. Says they can't even
  climb a pair of stairs.

*The stair ceremony fades away but the children in it divide
into two groups — one the Blazers Academy bunch and the
other the Shady Hill Continuation School bunch. Four
children in each group.*

SMITH:

Brown Minor, put that white mouse back in your pocket. And now all of you sing
your hearts out for that wonderful old school in that old Loyalist village by the
Atlantic Ocean — Blazer's Academy.

BLAZERS:

*They're all attired in black blazers, caps and skull and
crossbones.*

> Since eighteen hundred and three
> Blazer's Academy
> Has stood on its hill
> And evermore will
> For all the world to see.
>
> We always win at rugby
> Blazer's Academy
> We can twirl a billiard cue
> And play good polo too
> And will fight for Queen and Country.
>
> When we grow up we'll make money
> Blazer's Academy
> When we've raked it in the till
> We'll stand on this hill
> For all the world to see.
> Hurrah Hurrah Hurray! Blazer's Academy!

*After they've finished their song they spot MISS BIRD-
WHISTELL and her CONTINUATION SCHOOL KIDS. This
leads to an exchange of insults.*

BLAZERS:

> Hey, you Continuation School Rats
> When you see us coming
> Please raise your hats.

SMITH:

Quiet! Let the Shady Hill Continuation School scholars sing their school song.

BIRDWHISTELL:

Jimmie, whatever are you doing with that spool?

JIM:

It's my spool-knitting, Miss Birdwhistell. I have to keep doing it to calm my nerves.

BIRDWHISTELL:

The school song can take over then. Just put it in your pocket for now. Ready?

CONTINUATION SCHOOL KIDS:

> We have a school named Shady Hill
> And love it we always will
> Hrumpf hrumpf hrumpf hrumpf riddle me ree
> I'll never leave old Shady Hill.
>
> Frogs in the pond do splash about
> But never as happy as we
> Hrumpf hrumpf hrumpf hrumpf riddle me ree
> You will never chase us out.
>
> So here's to good old Shady Hill
> Where the best little trees get their start
> Hrumpf hrumpf hrumpf hrumpf riddle me ree
> From here may we never part.

They suddenly turn on the ACADEMY BOYS with:

> Academy dunces
> Sitting on the wall
> Shady Hill scholars
> Are better than you all.

SMITH:

"From here may we never part." Do you know, Miss Birdwhistell, I've always thought your school song remarkably prophetic. Do any of your scholars ever leave — by passing the final exam, that is?

BIRDWHISTELL:

Indeed, Mr. Stuffy-Smith, indeed. My children are just as clever and resourceful as yours although I will admit that polo is beyond them. Why don't we have a Geography Match between our two schools and just see. Children, when their side gives a geographical place name you must reply with another place name beginning with its last letter.

KIDS:

Nova Scotia	Albania
Asia	Arafura Sea
Alabama	Albany
Yucatan	New York
Kamloops	Saskatoon
Nigeria	Africa

BIRDWHISTELL:
Why not proceed with just Canadian names.

SMITH:
Very well. Boys — Canadian geography!

KIDS:

Saguenay	Alberta

BIRDWHISTELL:
No, Jenny. Saguenay ends with a "y" not an "a".

KIDS:

	Alberta, I mean Yukon
Nanoose	Eccles Hill
Levis	Scubenacadie
Estevan	Nipissing
Guelph	Hay River
Rimouski	Inuvik
Kitchener	Riviere du Loup
Prince Rupert	Tadoussac

pause

Canada	Arvida
Anse-a-Valleau	

pause

44

Algonquin Park	Upper Canada
	Kitimat
Thedford Mines	Spuzzum
Medicine Hat	Trois Rivieres
Sussex	X!

BIRDWHISTELL:

There is no X in Canada at the beginning of a place name.

BLAZERS:

We won! We won!

CONTINUATION SCHOOL KIDS:

Won by a trick! Won by a trick!

SMITH:

I'm afraid, Miss Birdwhistell, our school shows superior cunning. But so it would prove all down the line. Your scholars are drawn from all ranks of society. My scholars are upper-middle-class brats and — well, breeding tells.

BIRDWHISTELL:

Breeding tells, indeed!

SMITH:

Yes. For example, Miss Birdwhistell — there's a contest of rather an unusual sort for schools of children right now. I'm toying with the idea of entering my lads. If your school were to enter — which I don't suppose it would ever have the courage to — it's indubitable — Shady Hill wouldn't get a quarter of the way across.

BIRDWHISTELL:

Across what?

SMITH:

Across Canada. The Governor General took offence at a remark the Duke of Edinburgh made lately about the stamina of the Canadian child. The first group of children to cross the country in thirty days on a very limited budget will win a great prize of money for their school and for their own education.

BIRDWHISTELL:

Hear that, children? When you cross the country ahead of all the others we'll get enough money to buy a new pump for the school and send you all to Dalhousie

University.

JENNY:
Please, Miss Birdwhistell, could I use my share of the money to start a fish-and-chip shop?

BIRDWHISTELL:
Mr. Stuffy-Smith, Shady Hill will beat the pants off your Academy.

SMITH:
Oh, I say, Miss Birdwhistell, I do hope not.

They depart with kids singing their respective school songs which fit together contrapuntally.

WOLFWIND and MISS WEATHERGOOD enter with umbrellas. They close these as they enter MISS WEATHER-GOOD'S old house on a cliff by the sea. She sits in a rocking chair. We hear the sea; also the clock ticking on the mantle. WOLFWIND and MISS WEATHERGOOD are the Grizzly Bear and Coyote of the Indian legend whose struggle represents the battle between light and darkness. WOLFWIND is the Bay Street-promoter type. MISS WEATHERGOOD looks like the lean Maritimes spinster type — like L.M. Montgomery, but underneath there is always the suspicion of something else. WOLFWIND might wear a pair of furry motoring gloves — or be seen putting these on at the end of this scene.

There should be some way of presenting MISS WEATHER-GOOD'S house — a model house suspended or on stage — or flying through as they talk about it — at the end it should be shone upon with light. It is what the kids want to save, where they want to go. It is Canada. Perhaps cut-out trees, behind it, that make a green map of Canada.

WOLFWIND:
Thank you, Miss Weathergood, for showing me around the village. These old Nova Scotia villages by the sea must have lots of ghosts in them.

WEATHERGOOD:
Yes, Mr. Wolfwind. I suppose there are more ghosts up here than you're used to in New York City. There's good hunting too in the forest there upon the hill. Lots of deer, Mr. Wolfwind.

WOLFWIND:

Uh — no thank you, Miss Weathergood. I'm not very fond of venison. Wild honey's more my line. Any wild bees up there in the forest on the hill?

WEATHERGOOD:

Surely there must be, Mr. Wolfwind, in some of the older hollow trees. Why — the children have stopped singing.

WOLFWIND:

My dear Miss Weathergood, you do have sharp ears. The school's over a mile away.

WEATHERGOOD:

I need to have sharp ears, Mr. Wolfwind.

WOLFWIND:

And so, Miss Weathergood, you won't sell me this old wreck of a house of yours for six thousand dollars.

WEATHERGOOD:

Well, no. You see I was born in this house, Mr. Wolfwind. It's not that so much ever happened here:

James Wolfe never slept here
Nor Evangeline wept a tear

Here Tecumseh never took a scalp
Nor did Madeleine Vercheres ever scream "Halp!"

Laura Secord milked her cow somewhere else
And there too Sir Frederick Banting felt his pet dog's pulse.

Nothing's happened here at all except that
Seven generations of my people have trapped the rat

In the cellar, opened the door and whistled for the dog,
Fed the babies, lived off the high and the low of the hog.

WOLFWIND:

Sell it to me and I'll tear it down.
Get yourself an apartment — in Halifax downtown.

WEATHERGOOD:

Good gracious me, Mr. Wolfwind, are there human teeth as buttons on your waist coat? And what's that yellow old piece of parchment you keep putting back in your pocket when you think I'm not looking.

WOLFWIND:

So you won't sell. Well, Miss Weathergood, your cup of tea's been very nice and now I must get back to the Queen's Hotel. By the way I hear that the two schools in this village have entered the CROSS CANADA contest your Governor-General started.

WEATHERGOOD:

So I hear. We'll show that Duke of Edinburgh that our Canadian kids can climb a pair of stairs. Why they'll climb right up over and across Canada.

WOLFWIND:

Who do you hope wins, Miss Weathergood?

WEATHERGOOD:

The Shady Hill kids. They'll beat the pants off those Black Blazer Academy boys. I never laid eyes on such a horde of little snobs.

WOLFWIND:

The Shady Hill kids haven't got a chance, lady. I've been watching them play at recess — some of them don't get enough to eat and let's face it — kids from rural slums just aren't up to kids from rich homes.

WEATHERGOOD:

Is that so?! Look here, Wolfwind. I'll eat my shirt if I had one if those rich private school kids win. They're a bunch of spoilt brats. Now I like the Shady Hill scholars. Some of them show real get up and go.

WOLFWIND:

Kids have to have money behind them these days.

WEATHERGOOD:

They do not. What they have to have is — spirit. You old Philistine, how much will you bet me that Shady Hill wins.

WOLFWIND:

I'll bet you — fifty thousand dollars — if you bet me this old house, lady.

WEATHERGOOD:

It's a deal, Wolfwind.

> *They depart with their umbrellas and the children and their*
> *mentors enter for the start of the grand race.*

48

The morning it starts.

JENNY:

What are you kids gawking at?

BULLSEYE:

You'll never get across in thirty days.

TRANSY:

The feeling's mutual.

PIPER:

Bet you haven't even got a map.

JENNY:

Sure we have.

JIM:

A lovely map on this Canada Dry Ginger Ale bottle.

LUNETTE:

He's just kidding. We've got a good map in our geographies.

BULLSEYE:

What ya got all those old bottles for?

JIM:

It's the way we earn our pocket money. We collect empty bottles along the roadside.

BLAZERS:

Empty bottles. Any empty bottles. Rags and bones!

JENNY:

Do you wanta fight?

BULLSEYE:

Me fight a girl? I'm stronger than any girl.

JENNY:

I'll bet you aren't, Buster!

Pushing match between a girl and boy.

49

BIRDWHISTELL:

Now, children. Mr. Smith and I have just received the rules and the budget money. We'll follow you and be available any time you need us.

SMITH:

Get set, fellows. We're to start from the top of this cliff.

The cliff can be two chairs.

BIRDWHISTELL:

At one o'clock by the Dominion Observatory Official Time Signal!

SMITH:

Get set — and see you in Vancouver. Within thirty days.

The time signal sounds. The children get in their respective boats each with its flag. BLAZERS have a black stag: SHADY HILLERS have a green tree as their symbol. STUFFY-SMITH and MISS BIRDWHISTELL back away as if the children are rowing away from them.

BIRDWHISTELL:

Goodbye, my dears. I'll see you in Vancouver.

SMITH:

Good luck, Academy boys. Remember the school's honour is at stake.

KIDS:

Goodbye, Miss Birdwhistell. Goodbye, sir. We'll remember.

BULLSEYE:

Harder on the port stern there, Blubber Boy.

SQUEAK:

Please, Bullseye. Could I have half my biscuit ration right now?

BULLSEYE:

Pull at your oars, men. Harder. You'll have to wait, Squeak Squeak, no matter how hungry that mouse of yours is. No biscuit till we reach Newfoundland.

JENNY: *wielding a huge fantastic paddle*
Transy, you lazy bum, why ain't you rowing?

50

TRANSY:

I can't row and listen to my transistor set too, Jenny.

JIM:

Come on Transy or they'll beat us. Look they're over by those fishermen already.

> *Fishermen row up in their boat — the four adult actors in oilskins; they ahoy the BLAZER KIDS first.*

FISHERMEN:

Ahoy there, boys. Could you give us a hand with this four-hundred-pound halibut? It's fair pulling us out of our boat.

BULLSEYE:

My good man, we can't afford to stop for your fishing project.

BLUBBER BOY:

We're in a race to Vancouver.

LUNETTE:

We'll give you a hand, fisherman.

JENNY:

Hey! This fish is a real struggle to get into the boat.

JIM:

Do you ever fish for any other kinds?

Spouting whale	and a leaping dolphin
White sail, white sail	Plaice and halibut
Mackerel, tuna	Cod and shad
Alewives, smelt	Swordfish!
Salmon, pollock	Other flounders!
Spouting whale	and a leaping dolphin
White sail, white sail	Lobsters!

> *This catalogue explodes into a whole stage fish mime — which drifts off, fishermen and SHADY HILLERS, and BLAZERS drift on again. Use nets and mime — swordfish can be mimed as if one has just got TRANSY in the bottom, etc.*

BULLSEYE:

All right, blokes. I think we've done enough rowing. So — now that Smitty can't see us from the top of that cliff — my father sent me a 400-horsepower mini-boat motor.

He produces this.

SQUEAK:

It looks like an eggbeater, rather, don't you think, Bullseye?

BULLSEYE:

You *watch* your sharp tongue, Squeak Squeak, or I'll feed your pet to the cat. So I'll just put the eggbeater in and you can throw away your oars. Now — how's that? Aren't I your leader now?

OTHER BOYS:

Hurrah for Bullseye!

They throw away their oars. They make put-put sounds. The WHITE ICEBERG LADY now glides in over the sea.

ICEBERG:

Tell me who I am, little black-blazered boys.

BLAZERS:

Don't you know who you are, lady? Hey kids, what a stupe.

ICEBERG:

> My laughter causes terror
> I am a wonderful white lady
> Travelling over the waves
> Two thirds of me the blue wave hides
> My mother is soft and falls from the sky
> But I am as hard as a million granite grindstones
> Who am I?

BLAZERS:

How should we know? We're not good at riddles. Which way is Newfoundland?

ICEBERG:

Don't you want to know who I am?

BLAZERS:

Nah! We couldn't care less. Just tell us the way to Newfie.

ICEBERG:

> Boys, *Boys* — Newfoundland — is it that way.

> *They sail off and now come the CONTINUATION SCHOOL*
> *KIDS.*

JENNY:

> Gee — whillikers — pardon me, ma'am. But who are you?

ICEBERG:

> Aha! At long last — a child who is still curious.

> Tell me who I am.

> My laughter causes terror.

LUNETTE:

> It does!

> I am a wonderful white lady —

JENNY:

> Yes, yes.

> Travelling over the waves.
> Two thirds of me the blue wave hides.

JIM:

> Yes, yes.

> My mother is soft and falls from the sky.

TRANSY:

> Snow?

> But I am as hard as a million granite ivory grindstones.
> Who am I?

JENNY:

> I get it —

LUNETTE:

> You're an iceberg!

ICEBERG:

That's correct. Correct you are. My sister beat the *Titanic* in fair and open fight.
Now is there anything I can do for you?

JIM:

Which way to Newfoundland?

ICEBERG:

That way.

LUNETTE:

Did some boys in black blazers row by here lately?

ICEBERG:

Yes. Crackle crackle. But they aren't going to Newfoundland. They couldn't answer
my riddle — so I sent them to — Bermuda!

BLAZERS: *off in a corner as ICEBERG disappears*

Bermuda! How did we get to Bermuda! It'll take us days to catch up now. Those
Shady Hill kids will be sighting Newfie now — even rowing.

CONTINUATION SCHOOL KIDS:

Newfoundland! Here we sail round Newfoundland!

Chant and mime this antiphonally.

Malignant Cove	Boat Harbour, Ship Cove
Ireland's Blight	Goose Cove, Hare Bay
Hooping Harbour	Harbour Deep, Little Harbour Deep
Coney Arm	Jackson's Arm, Sop's Arm
Coachman's Cove	Pumbly Cove, Wild Cove
Indian Burying Place	Wild Bight, Lush's Bight
Comfort Cove	English Harbour, British Harbour
Ireland's Eye	Heart's Content, Angel's Cove
Trespassey Bay	Femme, Port-aux-Basques
Joe Batt's Arm	Cow Head, Parson's Pond

Deadman's Bay	Little Heart's Ease, Little Burnt Bay
Wolf Bay	Kegasha, Natachquan
Bear Cove	Daniel's Harbour, Doting Cove
Sault-au-Mouton	Ile-Michon Magpie
Goodbye Newfoundland	Goodbye Labrador
Goodbye Nova Scotia	and we've had such Maritimes
Goodbye Newfoundland	For we've come to Quebec!

The children mime beaching their boat. The old fort should
have some sort of representative prop.

JENNY:

Hey kids. It's getting dark. We'll have to camp here for the night. Tie up the boat with your spool knitting, Jim.

LUNETTE:

Look in the moonlight there. The ruins of an old, old fort.

An owl cries.

TRANSY:

Hey kids. I found an old bottle.

LUNETTE:

It's an old, old brandy bottle, Transy.

JIM:

Sh! Who's that under the tree there — over there?

LUNETTE:

It's a nun.

NUN:

Don't drink from that bottle, children. The poor and simple savages drank their death from it. Here. From this lily drink the dew of Times Past.

She sprinkles dew into their cupped hands from a lily.

It will make you dream. You will dream of what it used to be like long ago in Quebec — New France, as it was called then.

LUNETTE:

Are you the sister the Iceberg Lady talked about?

NUN:

No, my dears. She would be dressed in silver. My habit is that of a nun. Many years ago I lived in the convent here. Do you see this mark on my brow?

CONTINUATION SCHOOL KIDS:

Oh — it's a terrible wound and still bleeding.

NUN:

The hatchet of the Iroquois struck me there and I died. Now, children — what do you see in the moonlight?

CONTINUATION SCHOOL KIDS:

We see ladies and gentlemen dancing in old-fashioned costumes with fans and wigs and swords. Why are you giving Jimmie the horn?

NUN:

He is to blow it when he sees the Indians sneaking up through the forest. But go on show me how the lords and ladies used to dance in New France at this very place.

*The children imitate the minuet. Perhaps for a few moments
we see the people they see. Gorgeous, overpowering beauty.
Then — the horn blows, and the dancers vanish. The children
are alone in the fort.*

TRANSY:

Hey. Where'd the ladies and gentlemen go?

LUNETTE:

Those Indians look like the bloodthirsty kind.

*The BLAZER KIDS have come on dressed as Indians. The
SHADY HILL KIDS have retreated behind their fort. WOLF-
WIND holds a mirror up to assist the boys in adjusting their
feathers and warpaint.*

PIPER:

Bullseye, you look as if you've got a turkey gobbler on top of your head. Could I have the looking glass next, please?

56

WOLFWIND:

Good boys. We'll scare them out of that fort and right into the wilderness where they'll get hopelessly lost.

SQUEAK:

Ah yes, Mr. Wolfwind. If we win the race you get Miss Weathergood's house. What's so valuable about Miss Weathergood's house?

WOLFWIND:

You ever heard of Captain Kidd's treasure?

BULLSEYE:

You mean —

WOLFWIND:

Old Miss Weathergood's house was built smack on top of where he hid it. I came across an old map that proved it. Now — there'll be shares in that treasure for good boys who are of help to me.

PIPER:

Come to think of it, there'd better be. When the iceberg conked out our motor we rowed all the way to Bermuda.

WOLFWIND:

But I met you there and flew you back to here so you could catch up.

Enter MR. SMITH, who overhears.

SMITH:

What skullduggery is this? Are you trying to bribe the boys of Blazers Academy?

WOLFWIND:

I have bribed your boys. What are you meddling with my plans for? Boys. Part of Captain Kidd's treasure is yours if you bind him to that tree and gag him.

SMITH:

What is the school motto? Just tell me what it is before you gag me.

PIPER:

I know, sir. It's from the Bible. The trouble is if we don't truss you up Wolfwind and Bullseye here will beat the living daylights out of us.

BULLSEYE:

That's right, Piper. Sorry, sir, but we've got to win this race, fair or foul. Why aren't

57

you helping, Squeak Squeak?

SQUEAK:

I can't find my pet mouse. It's jumped out of my pocket.

BULLSEYE:

Never mind that. Sir, cross your hands.

Our attention now goes to the NUN and the SHADY HILLERS.

NUN:

Here are some drums.

CONTINUATION SCHOOL KIDS:

How are we going to defend the fort, Mother? We haven't got any guns.

NUN:

But you've got your minds. Pretend! Pretend as Madeleine de Vercheres did that there are hundreds of armed soldiers in the fort here. Here are some soldier's hats. Put them on poles and lift them — just above the palisade. Give commands. Beat the drum.

CONTINUATION SCHOOL KIDS:

But we don't know any French. They'll know it's just us.

NUN:

You know Canadian history, don't you? The first part of it is all French names. Just say them over.

CONTINUATION SCHOOL KIDS:

Qui vive la Montcalm.

LUNETTE:

Hey! Unpack my history book.

| Champlain | Talon | Laval | Bigot |

The BLAZERS answer with a war whoop.

PIPER:

Gee. Do you feel much like attacking?

BULLSEYE:

Where'd they get all those soldiers?

58

BLUBBER:
They're French soldiers like long ago.

CONTINUATION SCHOOL KIDS:

Brebeuf	Brule	Radisson	Dollard

SQUEAK:
Funny kind of French they're speaking. Hey! Look at those flags they've run up.

The French imperial flag and the Shady Hill flag.

WOLFWIND:
Give 'em some scarey Indian names:

BLAZERS' ENSEMBLE:

Abenaki	Micmac	Malecite	Naskapi
Montagnais	Algonkin	Mohawk	Iroquois
Oneida	Onondaga	Cayuga	Seneca
Beothuk			

LUNETTE:
The Beothuks are extinct.

BULLSEYE:
But the Iroquois aren't.

CONTINUATION SCHOOL KIDS:

Cartier	Frontenac	Hebert	Joliet
Lalemant	Vous avez brule les radissons!		

PIPER:
Well, I got that. They've burnt their radishes.

CONTINUATION SCHOOL KIDS:
Je n'aime pas Groseillers avec Radisson.

BLUBBER:
They're starving. They have to eat gooseberries mixed with radishes!

CONTINUATION SCHOOL KIDS:

Brulerons-nous les indiennes et leur amis?

BLUBBER:

Hey — I got that too. Shall we roast the Indians and their friends. Let's get out of here.

BULLSEYE:

Back to the boats, fellows.

WOLFWIND:

Chicken! Where's all your cadet corps training? Come on, give a whoop and shoot off those arrows I bought you.

> *They shoot the arrows and attack. The SHADY HILL KIDS*
> *sortie out yelling.*

Maisonneuve!   Maisonneuve!   Maisonneuve!

NUN:

Good, my children. You have frightened them away. Sometimes it did not always end that way.   *A cock crows.*   Farewell my dear children. May you, like Cartier and Champlain and the voyageurs, fare well up the River of Canada.

JENNY:

Golly. She's gone. What do we do now, Lunette?

LUNETTE:

Why it's morning.   *Cock crows.*

JIM:

Did we dream it all?

TRANSY:

Here's a fan — one of the dancing ladies dropped it.

JENNY:

We should be heading for Quebec City.

LUNETTE:

As the sister said — we go up the River of Canada. Come on kids. We'll walk along the banks.

> *They depart singing a voyageur song — "En roulant ma boule".*

60

Here's a song the boatmen used to sing going up this river. The St. Lawrence River. Last night I heard them singing it.

> *MISS BIRDWHISTELL enters, compass in hand, to discover*
> *STUFFY-SMITH tied to a tree.*

BIRDWHISTELL:

Mr. Smith! Whoever tied you to this tree?

> *She unties him.*

SMITH:

Miss Birdwhistell — my own boys. They've gone berserk. A dreadful chap named Wolfwind has bet 50,000 dollars they'll win and they're trying to knock your scholars right out of the race.

> *Picks up brandy bottle.*

BIRDWHISTELL:

Mr. Smith! I wouldn't drink from that ancient brandy bottle if I were you. It's at least three hundred years old and must be just pure fire water by now.

SMITH:

No, Miss Birdwhistell. I was just going to rub some on my mosquito bites — and my black fly bites. Do you mind?

BIRDWHISTELL:

Not in the least, Mr. Smith. Go right ahead. Where are your little devils right now?

SMITH:

While I was tied to this tree — on top of this cliff — I was able to observe that, when they fled in their boat and got out to sea, the Iceberg Lady started to chase them — up around Labrador and then — into Hudson Strait. So that finishes them, Miss Birdwhistell.

BIRDWHISTELL:

Cheer up. They're still going west. Shall we follow my children to Quebec City?

SMITH:

Why — we're there already! Here come your children with Quebec City. It's Carnival time and Bonhomme de Neige welcomes us all in our Geography Match.

> *Durer has a series of engravings in which a personage carries*
> *a model of Nuremberg platformed on a staff. Perhaps that*

61

*sort of thing now, with Bonhomme de Neige welcoming all
the children to the Carnival in a tableau. Fireworks. The
children sing the Carnival song:*

La chanson du Carnival

Refrain

Carnaval, Mardi Gras, Carnaval
A Quebec c'est tout un festival
Carnaval, Mardi Gras, Carnaval
Chantons tous le joyeaux Carnaval.

I

A Quebec a commence royalements
Par le grand joyeaux deploiements
Des tambours, des trompettes, des brillants
Que l'on voit dans les vrais couronnements.

II

Nos belles filles vaillamment se disputent
Le royaume de Quebec et ses buttes
Fin janvier on met fin a la lutte
En jouant jour l'elue de la flute.

*As the Carnival departs, the BLAZERS come on somewhat
listlessly drawing MR. WOLFWIND on a toboggan. They are
Eskimo dogs drawing him by thongs that radiate from the
front of the toboggan. From time to time they howl.*

WOLFWIND:
> Mush, you little varmints. The snow will all be melted before we get down to Toronto.
> How on earth did your boat get up to Hudson Bay?

BULLSEYE:
> That Iceberg Lady chased us in there, boss.

PIPER:
> Mr. Wolfwind, when are you going to give us something to eat?

BLUBBER:
> I'm not eating anymore botfly larvae squeezed out of caribou's backs and that's
> final. I'm writing to my parents the moment we get to a post office.

62

WOLFWIND:

There's a lot of money in Toronto. There used to be golden bathtubs in Casa Loma.

SQUEAK:

Look Mr. Wolfwind, we can't eat money.

WOLFWIND:

But food costs money. So make some.

PIPER:

How are we going to make money, Mr. Wolfwind?

WOLFWIND:

There's a big factory on strike. Lazy strikers! In you go, boys. Show your leadership qualities. Show them how you can work their factory and get some money for food.

BULLSEYE:

What's the raw material, boss?

WOLFWIND:

WOOD!

SQUEAK:

Give us some of it and we'll show how the factory here north of Toronto

PIPER:

TURNS our forest products into

BLUBBER:

all sorts of things.

*The boys line up and mime an assembly line that turns wood
into paper, into a pair of pink panties, into almost anything!
Improvise sound effects for this out of discarded drainpipes.*

BULLSEYE:
PIPER:

SQUEAK:
BLUBBER:

Hydraulic Barker

Rip the Bark off! Ouch!

The Chipper takes it over

Chip chip chip.

Soak soak soak.

Screen screen screen.
STEAM STEAM STEAM

Stir the digester and
Cook it in the chemicals

Hiss hiss hiss

Pulp pulp pulp

pulp pulp pulp

Blow upon it
    Blow upon it

Blow blow blow

Bleach it and whiten it

White white white

Press it down, press it down

Thinner and flatter

A piece of paper

Forever Amber!
Dick, Jane and Puff!

*The last boy at the end of the line will produce the manu-
factured object.*

Cut the trees down

Crack! Timber!

Bark that tree

Rip! Ouch!

Chip

Chip chip

Soak

Screen screen

Digest

Steam! Steam!

Cook

Hiss hiss

Pulp pulp

Pulp pulp

Blow

Blow

Bleach

Bleach

Acetic Acid

Ouch ouch ouch

Solvent!

Acetate acetate

Spin spin spin —

Ladies' lingerie

Spin spin spin

A red dress!

Spin spin spin

A plate of hamburger!

*They run off after the end boy whose machine produced the
hamburgers.*

64

WOLFWIND:

South, boys. That is where Toronto is. South!   *Exit.*

Enter the SHADY HILLERS holding on to each other in a line that represents Yonge Street.

ALL:

We're walking up Yonge Street from Union Station.

JENNY:

Big pillars!   *Looks up.*   Gray cement.   *Looks down.*

LUNETTE:

Secondhand books.

JIM:

There's a lady with man's pants on.

TRANSY:

CKEY! CHUM!

He holds transistor to his ear.

JENNY:

I'm scared. *All* those cars.

They make car noises.

ALL:

We're walking up Yonge Street from Union Station.

LUNETTE:

Oh Jenny, did you mail your letter to your mum?

JENNY:

Gee, no. I'll post it right now.

Kid in a red cloak walks past to give the effect of their passing a post-box.

JIM:

What's Chanel no.5?   *Holding nose.*

Looking in shop window sequence.

TRANSY:

>Ban for sale!

>*Really holding nose.*

>There's a guy in green shoes!

JENNY:

>Here's a sponge for sale.

LUNETTE:

>Ah — it smells of the sea — like the harbour back home.

JIM:

>Here, let me have a smell.

JENNY:

>Give it here, Lunette.

>*They run off after LUNETTE who runs away with the sponge to her nose.*

>*WOLFWIND and his band now enter.*

WOLFWIND: *enters with BLAZER KIDS*

>Now boys. When you get your share of Captain Kidd's Treasure you might want to come here to the Stock Exchange and invest it in the Stock Market. Here's where you buy and sell shares in our industries or your metals. You make a profit. You sometimes make a loss.

HOGTOWN STOCK MARKET!

Alberta Distillery! Sales 21000, High 99, Low 99, Closed 99

Atlantic Sugar! Sales 3835, High 17-5+8 dollars Low Closed

Bell Telephone   *Your sales call is now ready for you, sir.*   **High Low Closed**

>*This is a recorded announcement. The number you have dialed. Annie doesn't live here any more.*

Canadian Brewery	Sales	High	Low	Closed

Greyhound	*Wild fractions here, perhaps a low roar of sales High Low Closed, also some sort of juggling act.*
Husky Oil	
Salada Tea	
Mothers Parkers Tea	
Laura Secord Candy	
Toronto Weekly Mining	*percussion here; a chorus of metals*
Cobalt	Cobalt
Zinc	Bourlamaque
Nickel	Sudbury
Lead	Calumet
Copper	Flin Flon
Iron	Michipicoten
Steep Rock	Wabana and Marmora
Uranium	Port Radium
Platinum	Where does it come from?
Silver	Trail
Gold	Kirkland Lake, Fort Knox!
Coal	Estevan
Asbestos	Thetford Mines
Oil	Leduc!

BULLSEYE: *as if looking out window*
    Hey, Squeak Squeak. Guess who just passed by. Our public-school friends of SHADY HILL!

WOLFWIND:
    Let's get in some taxis and run 'em down, boys. They're not used to traffic in the big city.

This sequence should be mostly car noises made by kids,
horns and small mirrors which flash, held in the BLAZERS'
hands.

A ballet with the two groups of scholars.

RED!   **ORANGE!**   **GREEN!**

The CONTINUATION SCHOOL KIDS run and stop, pushed
this way and that by the traffic noises.

STOP!   **GO!**   **WALK!**   **DON'T WALK!**

Actual traffic signs could be used. A crossbuck could
indicate that the CONTINUATION SCHOOL KIDS had
put a railway train between them and their pursuers.

JIM:

Jenny, what if it says DON'T WALK! when I'm in the middle of the road? Do I
keep on walking across or do I stand still?

JENNY:

And let all those cars mow you down?

LUNETTE:

But it does say DON'T WALK!

TRANSY:

Hey! It's awfully quiet. What's happened?

JENNY:

I guess we're not in Toronto anymore. Gee, it's dark.

LUNETTE:

I'm so tired. Isn't that a haystack over there? Let's go to sleep on it.

JIM:

My, we ran a long way. I thought we'd never shake them off our trail.

JENNY:

Am I dreaming or is it that this haystack here is moving?

The stage has darkened.

68

HAIRY MAMMOTH:

You aren't dreaming, my child. You've all climbed on top of the ghost of a hairy mammoth.

JENNY:

Yikes! We have! What's a hairy mammoth?

HAIRY MAMMOTH:

I'm a huge elephant like the creature who used to roam about in southern Ontario ten thousand years ago eating pine cones. Before long all the big glaciers melted.

LUNETTE:

Then what happened to you?

HAIRY MAMMOTH:

It got to be too warm for us. And we kept falling into bogs. I fell into a bog in the swamp by the road here.

JIM:

Where are you taking us?

HAIRY MAMMOTH:

To the west of where you are. Nanabozho tells me to take you to Moraviantown.

TRANSY:

Who's Nanabozho?

HAIRY MAMMOTH:

Go to sleep. You'll find out soon enough.

JENNY:

Is he an Indian god? In Moraviantown?

LUNETTE:

My, a hairy mammoth is soft and you hardly notice him moving. He's so different from those — from those — cars in Toronto.

The mammoth lumbers off with the children.

The traffic lights fade away.

The scene changes back to MRS. WEATHERGOOD'S house. Clock, rocking chairs. Jenny's mother is visiting, with her recently received letter.

Both are in rocking chairs.

WEATHERGOOD:

So — Jenny and the Shady Hill kids have got as far as Toronto, up in Canada there. The most dangerous part of the country, I'd say.

Reading a letter

JENNY'S MA:

I'd agree there, Mrs. Weathergood.

WEATHERGOOD:

Are they ahead of those little scamps from the Academy?

JENNY'S MA:

That's just the oddest part of Jenny's letter. They're neck and neck and the Blazer boys have been trying to frighten them back.

WEATHERGOOD:

The little devils!

JENNY'S MA:

The Blazer boys tied their own teacher — headmaster Stuffy-Smith to a tree up near Quebec City.

WEATHERGOOD:

What?!

JENNY'S MA:

That man — the millionaire from the States with human teeth instead of buttons — he's always with the Blazer boys getting them out of their difficulties and helping them scare the Shady Hill kids.

WEATHERGOOD:

I knew it! He's cheating! I knew he'd cheat.

JENNY'S MA:

Well, don't take it so to heart, Mrs. Weathergood. My. You do look strange. Why is it —

WEATHERGOOD:

I've bet him this old house, don't you see, Mrs. White. I lose it if the Academy brats get to Vancouver before the Shady Hill kids do. Well — that's not going to happen. I'll get him — I'll get him — at the Rockies! In the pass — Mrs. White!

70

JENNY'S MA:

Goodness gracious me! Your hands have got terribly dark — and furry, Mrs. Weathergood. Are you sure you're feeling well?

WEATHERGOOD:

I've never felt better in my life. Here — have a bone. It's the best bone on the buffalo that died yesterday.

JENNY'S MA:

What a strange way to describe a cup of tea.

WEATHERGOOD:

Some more gristle, Mrs. White? Some more sinew? Or do you like marrow?

JENNY'S MA:

I'll take some cream — and sugar. I wonder —

WEATHERGOOD:

There's an old Indian legend you may not have heard of, Mrs. White. It's about Grizzly Bear, the Indian God of Darkness, and Coyote — the Indian God of Light. They had a battle long ago — in the Kicking Horse Pass and they're going to have it again. When those little kids get there — Grizzly Bear will be waiting to — stop them.

JENNY'S MA:

Who will this grizzly bear be?

WEATHERGOOD:

Wolfwind! Grizzly Bear has been disguising himself as Mr. Wolfwind.

JENNY'S MA:

Well, I sure hope my Jenny doesn't get eaten up by a bear. Who will save her — this Coyote, you say. Who is this Coyote? Mrs. Weathergood — what long ears you've got. What big teeth. You're changing into a — Coyote.

WEATHERGOOD:

And Coyote — the Indian God of Light, has been disguised as me all these years — Coyote has had to be Mrs. Weathergood, living alone in her old house. Not any more, Mrs. White. Have another bone? I'll save your daughter from the Grizzly Bear. Wolfwind — here I come!

> MRS. WEATHERGOOD — now a white-aproned coyote
> executes a madcap dance while JENNY'S MA runs screaming
> out. Then — the Coyote vanishes. All is quiet once more in

*the old house. Before the light fades we hear the ticking of
the clock.*

The SHADY HILLERS enter bearing cornstalks.

LUNETTE:

We're as far south as you can get in Canada, Jenny.

JENNY:

Whew, it's hot. I swear those fields of corn grow a foot every minute you look around. What are you listening to, Transy?

TRANSY: *broad grin*
Detroit! Chicago!

Rock and roll sounds here.

JENNY:

How's your spool knitting, Jim?

JIM:

Well, Jenny, I've knit this far. If we get some more wool when we get up to Fort William I guess I'll have spool knitted my way across Canada. *Enter TECUMSEH.*

TECUMSEH:

Watch out, children. Your friends, the Black Blazers, are after you and so is Wolf-wind. They aim to get you put in jail as vagrants so you'll never get across Canada.

JENNY:

What'll we do?

TECUMSEH:

Quick! Pretend to be scarecrows guarding these fields of cornmaiden.

*They all strike scarecrow attitudes as BLAZERS and WOLF-
WIND pour in.*

BULLSEYE:

Five scarecrows, eh? Seems rather a lot, don't you think, boss?

WOLFWIND:

Oh these farmers down here spare no expense. Look at this proclamation! How about that, kids.

72

PIPER:

Settlers in Upper Canada. Rise for freedom! Join the fight against British tyranny. Get your Kentucky rifles and coonskin caps down the river under the buttonwood tree.

SQUEAK:

Hey! It's dated 1813. October 5, 1813. Do you suppose there'd still be any coonskin caps left?

WOLFWIND:

It's not too late, boys. We can scare the Shady Hill brats back to Nova Scotia because they'll think we're the ghosts of the Yankees who beat the Canadians here at Moraviantown long ago. *They dash off.*

TECUMSEH:

Children, we are about to fight the battle of Moraviantown. You'll have to help get the cannon ready.

JENNY:

Sure thing, Mr. Tecumseh. But where are the cannonballs?

TECUMSEH:

We're too poor to have any. Wait till they shoot over some of their own. Then you see if they fit and fire them back. You'd better raise your battle flag.

JENNY:

Which flag should we raise, Lunette?

LUNETTE:

Well. We'll raise our Shady Hill school flag. The green shady tree.

TECUMSEH:

And I'll raise my totem — the tortoise.

JIM:

And we'd better raise this as well.

The flag of Canada is raised.

This stage picture is important — the green-tree flag on one pole, the lowest; then, the tortoise totem; and, on the highest pole, should come Canada's flag.

Now kids. Is this Canada's flag?

He points to tortoise.

Audience participation. (Expand or omit, as you see fit.)

TECUMSEH:

No. That is my emblem.

JIM:

Transy. Go and point out Canada's flag.

In a trance TRANSY points to the Shady Hill flag. His transistor is glued to his ear.

Is Transy right, kids? No, Transy, that's our school flag. So—

Pointing to our flag

whose flag is this?   *Audience participation.*   Right.

TECUMSEH:

Get thee ready. The black bow of the thunderous cannon is bent back. The Yankees fire. Now comes its furious murderous rolled up arrow-child.

The cannonade begins. A large basketball comes zooming in. This can be thrown back and forth. Lots of smoke. Lots of sound.

JENNY:

On — Canadian Infant Volunteers! Repel the foreign foe!

A toy sword and cap pistol fight. In come BLAZERS and WOLFWIND with Stars and Stripes, who win the battle.

BULLSEYE:

We've won, boss. On to the Fort! On to York!

PIPER:

Aw, did we kill them all?

WOLFWIND:

Captain Kidd's treasure, Piper. Good work, boys. Now on to Fort William.

The SHADY HILLERS arise from their death-positions and hobble about.

74

LUNETTE:

Aw. They've killed poor Tecumseh.

TECUMSEH:

No. I'm not quite dead yet, children. I do though miss all that skin they took off me to make whips and shoelaces. The souvenir business can be carried overly far. Just help me over that hollow log.

LUNETTE:

The Indians used to bury their dead in hollow logs.

TECUMSEH crawls onto the hollow log.

TRANSY:

Gee, he's completely disappeared into that hollow log.

JIM:

Look! There's an old turtle crawling out the other end. *Looking.* Tecumseh still in the hollow log? Why no. There's no one in the hollow log at all. I can see right through it.

LUNETTE:

That's the story of old Tecumseh, the great Indian chief who helped us in the War of 1812. He crawled wounded into a hollow log and came out changed into a tortoise. And some tortoises never die.

JENNY:

He wants to tell us something.

She kneels down.

He says he will take us on his back to Fort William where Nanabozho lives.

TRANSY:

Who's Nanabozho?

LUNETTE:

He's the god of the Indians. He lies asleep on top of Cape Thunder, high above Lake Superior.

JENNY:

He says — for us to climb on his back, shut our eyes and he will take us to Cape Thunder. We helped at Moraviantown. He will help.

The children get onto the tortoise's back. It can be one of those
trolleys they use in stores. As they go off, Cape Thunder rolls
on in front of the hollow log so TECUMSEH can get out,
yawn, stretch himself and fall asleep on Cape Thunder.

The children re-enter, perhaps crawling on their knees as if
crawling up the cliff.

JENNY:
   There he is. The sleeping giant.

JIM:
   Nanabozho!

LUNETTE:
   It's dangerous to wake him.

TRANSY:
   Why should we wake him anyhow?

LUNETTE:
   Perhaps — because he alone can tell us how to get to the Great Western Sea in time.

JENNY:
   Tecumseh, when he became a tortoise, told me that Nanabozho would only wake up
   if we were to name all the bodies of water that flow into each other from here — to
   the Atlantic Ocean. Where will this cup of water go?

JIM: *cupping hands*
   Into Lake Superior

ALL:
   which flows into

LUNETTE:
   the St. Mary's River

ALL:
   which flows into

TRANSY:
   Lake Huron, which flows into

76

JENNY:

the Clair River

ALL:

which flows into

JIM:

Lake St. Clair

ALL:

which flows into

LUNETTE:

the Detroit River

ALL:

which flows into

TRANSY:

Lake Erie

ALL:

which flows into Niagara Falls which flows into Lake Ontario which flows into the St. Lawrence River which flows into the Sea!

> *The water passes from hand to hand down the line of children —*
> *with a big mime at Niagara Falls and a spread out for the Sea.*

NANABOZHO:

Not since the day I fought with my father the cruel West Wind who killed my mother Loonwater have I felt so wide awake. Children with pure living hearts have awakened me.

JENNY:

Why are you sleeping up here on top of Cape Thunder, Nanabozho?

NANZBOZHO:

I had no more work to do. I had killed off all of the monsters. I had fashioned the land again after the great flood. But for children who know and love their country I awake once more. Cape Thunder, where I sleep, is in the very centre of the land. Look — do you see something white over there? In the east.

LUNETTE:

I see all the way down the lakes and rivers of Canada — to the White Lady who was the Iceberg.

NANABOZHO:

And what do you see over there — to the west?

JIM:

Across a great field of grass — I see mountains capped with snow.

NANABOZHO:

As I fall asleep again I will tell you how you will reach those mountains capped with snow. First you will meet — *He whispers to them.*

JENNY:

Muskeg Maggie! How will we get away from her?   *He whispers*

JIM:

Grizzly Bear in the Kicking Horse Pass. Grizzly Bear! How will we

> *More whispering as they push out NANABOZHO and Thunder Cape.*
>
> *As they do so Muskeg Maggie enters and falls asleep on the floor.*
>
> *She is a slatternly giantess covered with sporrans and purses round her belt and coin changing belts. Very tubby. Enter the children.*

JENNY:

Gee whiz, I'm scared of this forest. Hey, this is a ghost town.

> *JIM stands on top of MUSKEG MAGGIE.*

Leaping lizards, there's an abandoned steam engine —

LUNETTE:

Let's get it going and go across the prairie. How do you light the boiler now?

TRANSY:

Hey Jim, you're standing on something.

LUNETTE:

Don't move. If we wake her up we're done for. She's the Muskeg ogress Nanabozho spoke of. She lurks in the forests of northern Ontario and swallows up travellers.

78

Don't wake her up, Jim.

> *Very gingerly, JIM steps off the giantess, but then TRANSY'S transistor radio blares out. Frantic efforts to turn it off.*

JENNY:
Can't you turn that bloody thing off, Transy! Why's it going so loud?

TRANSY:
Aw, pipe down yourself — be quiet, stop shouting!

> *The rock and roll from the transistor radio stops just as MUSKEG MAG awakes.*

LUNETTE:
Jenny, keep her amused and remember what Nanabozho told you, while we get the old steam engine going.

> *Behind the ogress's back, three of the children push the old steam engine out. It can be some sort of device with a cut out smokestack hat and cowcatcher apron on an actor.*

MAG:
Bring me that wagon, girl. I want to suck it into my muddy depths — people and all.

> *She devours the toy wagon.*

I'm tired of eating just mooses. It's iron I crave. Bring me those bulldozers! I'll get some of my own back. I'll have that radio that wee chappy, that weasely chappie's got.

> *She doesn't turn, but we realize that she has an eye in the back of her head.*

TRANSY:
She can't have my transistor set — it's my brain!

JENNY:
He doesn't want to give it to you, Muskeg Mag. Give it to her, Transy!

MAG:
Then I'll eat you all up.

TRANSY:

I'll get you for this, Jenny.

Hands over transistor set.

JENNY:

It's not my fault, Transy. Here, ma'am.

MAG:

Thank you.

Swallows transistor set.

Who stole my gold? What you got in your purse, Jenny?

JENNY:

Just one nickel.

MAG:

You stole that from one of my mines. From one of my nickel purses. All right, girlie. I'll give you one last chance. If you can answer these three riddles I'll fall fast asleep for forty seconds, giving you a chance — a chance to get away. Okay?

JENNY:

Gotcha.

MAG:

What's this?

A hand riddle.

JENNY:

The other half of this.

Puts up her hand.

MAG:

And this?

JENNY:

A spider walking on a looking glass.

MAG:

And what's this?

JENNY:

It's a — it's a — it's a looking glass walking on a spider.

MAG:

Awhoohrrh —

She falls down snoring; voices count to forty all the while.

JENNY:

Kids, we have exactly forty seconds in which to get out of here on that steam engine. Can we do it?

LUNETTE:

We can't get the fire started under the boiler, Jenny. Our geography book just won't light.

JENNY:

Transy. In with the gum cards.

TRANSY:

My gum cards!

He throws them into the steam engine's furnace, one by one.

LUNETTE:

There — it's starting. Get set, kids. I believe we pull this lever and —

Despairingly, TRANSY recites the names of pop-singing groups as he throws the cards into the furnace.

LUNETTE:

The race is on — All — to the rocky mountains.

With a roar, the ogress awakes, but they are too fast for her.

The trains can be lines of children snaking this way and that.

SHADY HILL KIDS:

Fort William   West Fort William

Murillo   Kaministiqua

Finmark, Buda   Raith, Savanne

Upsala, Niblock

English River

Martin, Bonheur

Ignace, Osagnan

Wabigon, Dryden

Oxdrift, Minnitake

Pine Hawk Lake

Scovil, Kenora

Keewatin, Whitemouth

Shelley, Julius

*Enter the BLAZERS and WOLFWIND with their train and
they chant:*

Sioux Lookout

Hudson

Red Lake Road

McIntosh, Farlane

Redditt

Minaki

Ottermere, White

Winnitoba, Hector

Elma

Anola

WINNIPEG:

SHADY HILLERS:

Molson, Lydiatt

Cloverleaf, Hazelbridge

Oakbank, North Transcana

WINNIPEG!

BLAZERS:

Elie

Portage la Prairie

Deer

Shilo

North Brandon

Brandon!

*There are obvious train sounds, of course, but one of my
favourites is that haunting change of tune the crossing bells
make as you whizz by them. Also the old steam whistle.*

WOLFWIND:
Okeydoke, lads. Here at Brandon we're going to switch on to the CPR track and
head east!

SQUEAK:
Why head east, Mr. Wolfwind? Isn't that backward?

WOLFWIND:
Will you never understand? We have to eliminate the Shady Hill kids. If they win we don't get Captain Kidd's treasure. So we collide with them and wreck their chances forever.

PIPER:
Don't go back now, fellows. We're winning. Who cares about the —

BULLSEYE:
Do as Wolfwind says, or I'll confiscate your pipe, Piper.

PIPER:
Very well. You know I have to smoke it on doctor's orders — to calm my nerves.

BULLSEYE:
Get those wheels moving! —

Their train shunts off.

SHADY HILLERS:

Rosser Meadows   Poplar Point

High Bluff   Portage la Prairie

Burnside

JENNY:
Hey! Do you hear something coming towards us?

JIM bends his ear to the track.

Do you hear anything, Jim?

JIM:
We gotta back up, kids. There's a mad steam engine coming towards us. Back up quick.

Austin   MacGregor   Bagot

Burnside   Portage la Prairie High Bluff

Poplar Point	Marquette	Meadows Rosser
WINNIPEG	**Crash!**	Kenora —

The BLAZERS have joined the chant and crash into the
SHADY HILLERS who fall off the track — but

JENNY:

Get on those jiggers, kids. Look at them there, on that siding. Off we go.

They mime the Buster Keaton kind of jigger.

LUNETTE:

Over the Rocky Mountains!

BULLSEYE:

After them! They jumped off and got on those jiggers. We gotta turn this train around!

SQUEAK:

We can't turn around, you idiot. We've got to back it up!

WOLFWIND:

You little monsters. You just ran that train over my foot. Wait up, boys. Wait up for me. I'll chase you , you little devils.

BULLSEYE:

On for the Rockies. Get steam up. We'll go backwards all the way to Kicking Horse Pass.

BLUBBER:

Shovel the coal in faster, Squeak Squeak. Mr. Wolfwind is really mad at us. Look at him.

Exit pursued by WOLFWIND — the boys go forward, backward!

Cut to darkness, wind and snow. Enter the SHADY HILLERS
with lanterns fighting their way up through the Kicking
Horse Pass.

LUNETTE:

Jenny, I can't go on. I'm too tired and my lantern's gone out.   *Coughing*

JENNY:

The cave can't be much farther, Lunette. We can rest there and get warm by a

84

fire. See — there's a light up there. See it, Jim.

JIM:

Yes. Let us help you, Lunette. Lean on Jenny and me. See the lantern up there? It won't be long now.

TRANSY:

My lantern's gone out. Why'd we ever go on this trip? We'll never get over the mountains. I'm turning back.

JIM:

You keep saying that, Transy.

JENNY:

How come our lanterns are going out?

JIM:

We put plenty of coal oil in them. Jenny, I'm going to throw my spool knitting up at that rock by the cave. We can follow the knitting in the dark then if —

He throws up the spool and the knitted line follows it.

JENNY:

Did it catch hold of something, Jim?

JIM:

Something up at the cave has got hold of it. Now everybody grab hold of this spool knitting and it'll lead us to the cave.

TRANSY:

I want to go back.

JIM:

Can't go back now, Transy.

They fade away and another lantern enters. We are now with WOLFWIND and the BLAZERS.

WOLFWIND: *his bear costume over his arm*
Well, Blubber Boy, do you see the Shady Hillers' lanterns down below?

BLUBBER BOY:

Yes, sir. They're climbing up towards us.

WOLFWIND:

> And do you know what?

SQUEAK:

> I know what I think, Mr. Wolfwind. You wouldn't let me look for my pet mouse down there in the pass and now I'll never see him again.

WOLFWIND:

> Are their lanterns still alight?

BULLSEYE:

> Two of theirs have gone out, Mr. Wolfwind.

WOLFWIND:

> Ahah!

PIPER:

> If I may ask, sir, why are you putting on that bear costume?

WOLFWIND:

> Ouch! Who threw that?

SQUEAK:

> It's a piece of spool knitting, sir. Here's the spool.

WOLFWIND:

> Ahah! Give it to me. Now — put out our lantern. Hide yourself. Give me that spool.

> *In the snow and semi-darkness the SHADY HILLERS come on, also holding the line.*

JIM:

> We should be at the cave about now. I recognize the knots where I was knitting this morning.

LUNETTE:

> There's someone over there, Jim.

JENNY:

> Hello. Are you holding the end of our line?

> *The lights come up and the SHADY HILLERS see that the other end of the line is held by a GRIZZLY BEAR.*

86

JIM:

Yikes, kids, a grizzly bear. Drop that spool, you grizzly bear.

LUNETTE:

Watch out. He's pulling us closer towards him.

JENNY:

If we drop it, he'll drop it and come running after us. Pull!

> *The BLAZERS come out and pull with the help of GRIZZLY BEAR. They pull the SHADY HILLERS towards a crevice in the rocks.*

> *Trap door.*

Help! They're pulling us over a big hole that goes down, down, down.

JIM:

I want my spool knitting back. Pull for Shady Hill.

COYOTE: *leaping in*

I'll help you Shady Hill kids!

> *She pulls and GRIZZLY BEAR and his team fall flat on their faces.*

GRIZZLY BEAR:

So — Coyote. We meet again.

> *He rises for a duel.*

COYOTE:

Get out of here — Grizzly Bear alias Wolfwind.

GRIZZLY BEAR:

The same to you, Coyote — alias Miss Weathergood.

COYOTE:

I think I know how to handle you.

GRIZZLY BEAR:

You contemptible coyote in a white apron — with your common scruffy little cubs. I'll make it so dark they'll never be able to see their way over the mountain.

Dark! Dark! Dark! Let it always be dark!

COYOTE:

Light! Light! Light! Let it always be light!

*They chant in competition — when COYOTE is loud it is
light, when GRIZZLY BEAR is loud it darkens.*

GRIZZLY BEAR:
Whewh! I'm worn out. Let's make it a draw. Have it dark half the time, light half
the time.

KIDS:

And that is why the dark of night
Is balanced by the dear, sweet daylight.

GRIZZLY BEAR:
Coyote.....you sneaky dog in a white apron, I know there's one thing you can't beat
Grizzly Bear at, and that's being silent. If you break silence before I do, so much
snow will fall that your children will be snowbound in the Kicking Horse Pass forever and winter in Canada will be three months longer.

COYOTE:
Let the great silence begin the next time the Great White Owl cries. Children —
be extra-special-silent.

The owl cries.

*JENNY has to hold her hand over TRANSY'S mouth, since she is
shaken with silent giggles. It is GRIZZLY BEAR, however,
who giggles aloud and starts to undo the bear costume.*

WOLFWIND/GRIZZLY BEAR:
Halp! Let me out of here. I'm being tickled to death.

SQUEAK:
It's my mouse, Mr. Wolfwind. It got away from me, you will remember, and you
wouldn't let me search for it in Saskatchewan. So — it built a nest in your grizzly
bear costume.

COYOTE:
Wolfwind! You are beaten now. After him, children. Take off his disguise and send

him packing. My faithful ally, Little Mouse, has come to my aid again, as long ago.

JENNY runs after WOLFWIND and returns with a bearskin.

JENNY:
Here you are, Coyote.

COYOTE:
And what happened to Mr. Wolfwind, Jenny?

JENNY:
He's hiding way back in the cave — laughing helplessly as ten little mice crawl over him looking for biscuit crumbs.

SQUEAK:
My mouse was a she!

COYOTE:
Silence, children. Dawn is coming and at dawn you may start. This time the race will be fair. It will depend on the intelligence and cunning and strength of each of you. Here is

Enter SIMON FRASER.

my friend Simon Fraser. He will take each one of you down the Fraser River through Hell's Gate as far as Chilliwack. From there, you have one day left in which to reach the sea — under your own steam. I will not help you. Wolfwind will not be able to help you little rats because I am going to shut him up in this cave for a while.

Mr. Fraser, are you ready to take these children down?

FRASER:
Aye, ready, Coyote. But are they worthy to go down to the sea with me — down the river I discovered.

COYOTE:
We'll soon find out. Before I let any boy or girl out of here he must tell me a song about one of my brothers, he must not tell which brother it is, and he must guess what animal another's song is about. Lunette, which one of my brothers do you sing?

LUNETTE:
This one:

I am a pincushion, needle cushion
I'm stuck full of needles and pins
Come close and you'll find
They're wrong way IN!

COYOTE:

Now, Master Piper, do you guess what Lunette is pretending to be?

PIPER:

Oh — she's pretending to be a porcupine.

COYOTE:

Right. Now, Piper, you give Lunette a riddle about one of my brothers.

PIPER:

Suddenly glimpse me. A flash of fire.
I see you see me and under the fence wire
In an instant I am into the dark woods my home.

My children dance in the moonlight while
I visit the farmer's farmyard.
I've got a fat goose. Hark to that barking.
Now I must run very hard.

LUNETTE:

That's a fox.

JIM:

I'm a fat and lazy rodent
My dugout's in the clover field
I'll eat almost any green thing — even a thistle!
On my doorstep I stand like this
And look at you — then disappear with a WHISTLE!

SQUEAK:

You're a groundhog. See if you can guess this.

I'm a mouse of the air
Flitter flutter everywhere
My where is there!
In the twilight's star pinned dusky hair.

JIM:

A bat.

JENNY:

Try this one.

Though I have a voice like a diesel train,
I am not a train
I have a bell at my neck
But it doesn't ring.

Though I've got horns
I am not a cow
I've got legs like stilts
But I'm not a clown.

BLUBBER:

A moose!

Stickem up! I'm a robber!
Though I leave tracks like a barefoot kid.
Six rings on my bushy tail!
When the harvest moon is up I'm hid.
Within the cornfield seeing if it's ripe.
The banks I rob — of mice and grasshoppers
I like to fish by the light of the moon
Call me what you will, but I'm a

JENNY:

Raccoon!

COYOTE:

Now, Simon Fraser. Those are all the children fit to go down the Fraser River with you.

FRASER:

What about those two over there, Coyote?

COYOTE:

Those two over there. They don't want to go down to the Pacific Ocean do they?

TRANSY:

Yes, I do.

COYOTE:

 Well, then, make up a riddle about one of my brothers.

TRANSY:

 I can't.

COYOTE:

 Do you know why you can't?

TRANSY:

 No. Well, sort of.

COYOTE:

 Because you've been dishonest and betrayed your friends.

TRANSY:

 Yes.

COYOTE:

 You accepted a bribe from Wolfwind and you filled up those lanterns with water instead instead of coal oil, so they'd go out.

TRANSY:

 I was so mad at losing my gum cards and my transistor radio.

COYOTE:

 Well.

TRANSY:

> Running always running far away
> Beneath the owl and before the bear
> What can I do but be as many as I may
> Be humble and coloured as the summer ground.

 Changes into a white coat.

> Now the ground has turned white. What will I do?
> Can the small, the fearful and the weak survive?
> Of course. If they give up their vanity
> And turn white — too.

COYOTE:

 Now, Bullseye. Can you guess what that is?

BULLSEYE:

No.

COYOTE:

Because your mind is choked with badness, isn't it?

BULLSEYE:

Yes.

COYOTE:

Badness such as —

BULLSEYE:

I cheated with the boat motor. And I left poor Stuffy-Smith tied up to a tree in Quebec. And — I bully people. Because I'm weak.

COYOTE:

Good. Now if you admit you're weak, you can start to be strong.

BULLSEYE:

My presence is noticed
Far and wide through the wood
Where I've been is thought of
As not terribly good.

Don't come to close, I say
I'm stamping the ground
Don't you hear my teeth chatter
I've got more too than just sound.

Though I'm small — start running
I've discovered one way to be strong
Hit the enemy on the nose;
But not with a rose!

TRANSY:

A skunk.

COYOTE:

Now. You all may go with Simon Fraser down his river but first — since you have all been humble and been animals like me, I will let you be human again — because I can be human again.

COYOTE whirls about and about and turns into MISS WEATHERGOOD.

KIDS:

Miss Weathergood!

WEATHERGOOD:

Don't stand there gawking! Down the Fraser River.

As children climb up and slide down a slide the whole company mimes and paddles and chants.

Use fish kites to suggest salmon coming up.

Use a long piece of blue silk to suggest the river.

From Fort George

Down

Down the Fraser River

To the Sea.

These are the sand bars of the Fraser; these rivers and creeks flow into the Fraser River.

Road River	Envoyons!
Naver Creek	Envoyons!
Stove Creek	Envoyons!
Big Bar Creek	Down:
Rapide Couverte	Grande Rapide
Woodpecker River	Fort a gauche
Soda Creek	Chimney Creek
Risk Creek	Alkali Creek
Dog Creek	Gaysard Creek
French Bar	Watson Bar

Yulahan River		Lillooet
Texas Creek		Stein River
Thompson River!	*Big climax here and then fade away.*	Camchin
Boston Bar		Hell's Gate
Spuzzum	*Roll out the slide.*	Mills Bar
Emorys Bar		Chillukeyuk River
Chilliwack		
The Sea!	The Sea!	The Sea!

*Enter BIRDWHISTELL and SMITH with umbrellas. SMITH
has just been using a pair of binoculars.*

*At the back of the stage stand the SHADY HILL children
hidden by great coloured umbrellas.*

SMITH:
O dear, Eunice. It looks as if my brats are going to win.

BIRDWHISTELL:
If they do, Stuffy, I'll burst into tears. Strange though — we'd never have got over the mountains if it hadn't been for the spool knitting thread Jim kept knitting out behind him. He must be in front of us somewhere.

Enter the BLAZERS.

BULLSEYE:
Sir, we don't deserve to but we —

SMITH:
Yes, you young devils, you've

BIRDWHISTELL:
And we were going to buy a new pump for the school.

SHADY HILLERS down their umbrellas.

JENNY:
We think we won. But we'll share the prize money if you like. If Mr. Smith and Eunice — Oh I beg your pardon — Miss Birdwhistell — Are you going to get married —

why don't our schools join too?

BLAZERS:

Jolly good idea that! Co-education!

BIRDWHISTELL:

Jimmy, have you wound up *all* the spool knitting you've been doing — *all* across Canada.

JIM: *producing a huge ball of yarn*

Yes, Miss Birdwhistell. Sometimes it gets stuck. Like it gets stuck on Mr. Wolfwind, but I wind him in. Or Miss Weathergood. Or

These people come in attached to the thread.

someone in this very theatre.

A prepared audience member is pulled in.

While the actors sing — the first flag tableau and ladder ritual is re-enacted.

As the Canadian child — BLUBBER BOY — proudly climbs the ladder with our flag and the other flags unfurled we hear the counter-pointed school songs, and also the following:

> From east to west we walk
> Across our country
> Forests and cities do we view
> People from the past too
> As we walk from sea to sea
> *A mari usque ad mare.*

96

Names &
Nicknames

A Note for Names & Nicknames

This story takes place in the southwestern Ontario hamlet of Brocksden around 1900. The play was written with a bare stage in mind; all the stage setting can be accomplished with words, pantomime, the human body, music from rhythm band instruments, the audience themselves. Nothing should stand in the way of a flowing story line that proceeds without a break until the very last chorus. Dress the stage with a stepladder; when Thorntree climbs up on the roof to listen down the chimney this stepladder is all that is needed. A great many items in this play are meant to be expanded and improvised upon — all the time keeping in mind the insistent rhythm and flow of the story line; for example, try dividing up a chorus with one-half chanting a basic repetitive line while the other half does a whole stanza.

Many of the choruses, by the way, are taken from the suites of words used in a speller that my father learned to spell out of in the 1890's at the Irish School near Stratford, Ontario; scenery choruses came from such word lists as "In the Yard" and "On the Farm." The great monumental lists of boys' and girls' names in this book gave me the idea for the climax of the play. Perhaps this might suggest to children, plays they could make up from gum cards, telephone directories, even arithmetic books!

All scenes take place on Farmer Dell's Farm. The time changes from summer to winter, to summer again, then to fall, to winter and back to summer.

Suggestions for an introduction: the actors line up before the audience and tell who they are in real life; who they are in the play. Have a discussion with the actors and gradually the audience about their names — first, middle and last. "How many Mary's in the audience? How many Peter's? Ask what their nicknames are. Can you guess what my nickname is/was? Since the whole business of nicknames is touchy don't carry this too far. In the Winnipeg production though, a very shrewd member of one audience did guess the nickname that one of the actors had lived with as a ten-year-old: "Nelly."

Names and Nicknames was first performed at the Manitoba Theatre Centre in Winnipeg, Manitoba, in October, 1963, with the following cast:

Mrs. Dell	Martha Henry
Farmer Dell	Heath Lamberts
Etta	Suzanne Grossman
Rob	Nelson Philips
Reverend Hackaberry	Garrick Hagon
Grandpa Thorntree	Ted Hodgeman
Baby One	Anita Cera
Baby Two	Blair Graham
Children	Christine Kirby, Debby Feldbrill
	Craig Parks, Anita Cera
	Blair Graham, Robert Elias
	Sheera Waisman, Angela McLeod
	Meredith Moore, Randy Benson
	Debby Crookes, Sharon Beckstead
	Debby Konowalchuck, Pam Macdonald
	Sherry Israels, Mary Cox
	Nancy Goyman, Joanne Knonpada
	Joanne Gregory, Elizabeth Graham
	Richard Gillman
Soprano Solo	Carla Israels

Directed by John Hirsch and Robert Sherrin
Music by Kenneth Winters
Sets and Costumes by Ted Korol

CHARACTERS

OLD GRANDPA THORNTREE	a trapper
FARMER DELL	
FARMWIFE DELL	
COUSIN ETTA	the hired girl
ROB	the hired man
REVEREND HACKABERRY	
BABY ONE	
BABY TWO	
BABY THREE	a large doll in christening dress
A CHORUS OF AT LEAST SIX CHILDREN	

**CHORUS AND
CHIEF ACTORS:**

 **The farm in the morning. The Farm
 Farmer Dell's Farm**

   *For the next sequence, the six chief actors mime the words
   they are saying. For "copse" they bring uplifted hands
   together and someone whistles a bird song. For "barn" they
   build a barn, and so on. Not every word gets a gesture and
   the whole thing must be kept flowing, but the actors do say
   these words with their bodies as well as their mouths.*

 **Vale hill dell dale
 Bush rock bank field
 Pool wood pond creek
 Ridge hedge copse yard**

Swale lane fence wall
Path road ditch post
Barn shed tree house

Farmer Dell's Farm

*The actors lie down as a rooster crows, some of them on the
benches. Now, the sleeping DELLS bestir themselves. There
can be mime of dressing, alarm clocks, etc. ROB, the hired
man, goes out to get the cows. The CHORUS utter moos and
some of them pretend to be cows.*

ROB:

I get up in the morning and go and fetch the cows.
Cobossy coboss Cobossy coboss

Ad lib repetition.

CHORUS:

Moo moo moo moo

ROB:

Come on cushy cows and come to be milked.

CHORUS:

Moo

Select two female members of the CHORUS to be cows.

ROB: *he drives them with a stick*
Here — here's the shortest way.

CHORUS:

Moo. We have to follow our cowpath.

ROB:

And it winds up and down.

CHORUS:

Our names are Blossom, Josephine, Moo, Rachel, Betty, Moo. Next year, let's make
the path curve more here. Rachel, Betty, Blossom and Josephine. Not too fast or
we won't let down our milk.

ROB:

Coboss coboss coboss coboss.

CHORUS:

Moo.

FARMER DELL:

Come cushy cows and we will milk you.

He and Rob mime this with pails and milking sounds.

The moos and milking sounds slowly change into the sound of a cream separator, which ROB turns while DELL pours in milk. An actor turns about pretending to be the revolving cream separator. Perhaps over to one side we also see the women preparing breakfast.

ROB:

Turn the separator, turn the separator.
Cream out one spout. Skim out the other.
Turn the separator, turn the separator.

CHORUS:

The bell goes tink tink tink.

FARMER DELL:

If the bell goes, you're turning it too slow.

CHORUS: *faster and fade*

Tink tink tink tink.....

ROB:

Sorry, Sam. I'm still half asleep.
Turn the separator, turn the separator.
Cream out one spout. Skim out the other.
Turn the separator.....

Slows down.

CHORUS:

Tink tink

ROB: *faster*

Cream out one spout. Skim out the other.

The pig sequence is about to start. This will take some humility, but it's worth trying. Everyone crouches down at their troughs and makes a rich oinking sound as FARMER DELL and ROB feed them.

FARMER DELL:

We get up in the morning and fetch the cows
And then we milk them
And then I slop the pigs and the cows
And then I count them
ONE FIVE TEN FIFTEEN TWENTY
little pigs.

CHORUS:

One five ten fifteen twenty little pigs.
Oink oink oink oink oink

A rising frenzy of sound — pigs at the feeding trough.

FARMER DELL:

Hey Rob! One of them's got away!
Nineteen little pigs!

They pursue the runaway pig, who leads ROB into the pig wallow — from which he emerges a dripping pillar when the pig is caught and returned.

ROB AND FARMER DELL:

One Five Ten Fifteen Twenty little pigs.

CHORUS:

Oink oink oink oink oink oink

ROB takes out a harmonica and plays it to the pigs. At certain points in his piece, one pig will stop eating and look up in rapture.

Now the horse sequence starts. Two of the CHORUS can be the horses. Two of the CHORUS can sit on the bench and drum with noise sticks to imitate the sound of their hooves.

FARMER DELL:

Rob, go now and catch the horses.

108

ROB:
Which ones, Sam? Sandy and Charley or Bradley and Dobbin?

FARMER DELL:
Today, we're sowing oats and barley, so hitch up the sorrel horse and Old Charley.

ROB: *with pail of oats and a rope*
Here Bradley

Whistles in a neighing way.

Here Charley   *whistles*

CHORUS: *two gallop about and are very hard to catch*
We won't come. We won't come.
We want to eat grass and play in the sun.

ROB:
Here Bradley
Here Charley   *whistling*

CHORUS:
We won't come. We won't come.
We want to eat grass and play in the sun.

With a drum, quite a race can be suggested, but eventually, after much neighing and hitching, the horses are caught and hitched to a seed drill — a bench.

**CHORUS AND
FARMER DELL
AND ROB:** *interspersed*
Harnessing horses.
Harnessing horses.
Collar and hames collar and hames
Lift up the neck yoke
Tongue tongue tongue
Tache up the traces to
Whipple trees double trees whipple trees
Whipple trees double trees whipple trees

ROB:
Ouch! You stepped on my foot, Charley.

*FARMER DELL drives off while ROB hops about on one
foot.*

FARMER DELL:

Giddup, Bradley. Up there, Charley

This oats and barley we've got to be sowing

Must get it in so it can start growing

Giddup, Bradley. Git up there, Charley

Gee! Bradley! Gee! Charley!

Haw! Bradley! Haw! Charley!

MR. THORNTREE appears.

*Now, a transition sequence. Don't be afraid to let the "knee
deep" sound carry on. Gradually, it will change into the
harsher sound of the THORNTREE sequence.*

CHORUS:

So spring on Farmer Dell's Farm.

The snow has melted, the snow has gone

Tra la la   Tra la la   Tra la la

The bare trees have put their green leaves on.

Tra la la   Tra la la   Tra la la

Knee deep   knee deep   knee deep   knee deep

The frogs in the pond sing

Knee deep   knee deep   knee deep   knee deep

The frogs in the pond sing.

*They hum, a sound interrupted by various farm noises — a cow
mooing. FARMER DELL shouting at the horses, a bird
whistling, frog song dying away. Slowly, a chorus of crows
cawing is built up and reaches a peak as GRANDPA THORN-
TREE enters and dominates the stage. FARMER DELL and
the HIRED MAN have faded away.*

CHORUS:

Caw caw caw caw

Caw caw caw caw

Raw raw raw raw

Raw raw raw raw

Old Grandpa Thorntree. Old Grandpa Thorntree.

Old Grandpa Thorntree. Old Grandpa Thorntree.

A ragged, gnarled old man enters with the remains of a top

*hat on his head. It is the top hat and the cane that make him
into THORNTREE. When last we saw him, he was one of the
horses, one of the men around the Dell farm.*

THORNTREE:

You children always tease me.
You children always tease me — you kids!

Members of the CHORUS jump forward and mock him.

CHORUS:

Haw haw haw. Old Mister Thorntree
Swallowed a peck of rusty nails
Spits them out and never fails
To make them twice as rusty
To make them twice as rusty.
Swallowed a peck of rusty nails
Spits them out and never fails
To make them twice as rusty
To make them twice as rusty.

THORNTREE:

Brat! How can I carry on my profession with you kids putting me in such a bad
temper all the time.

CHORUS:

What is your profession?

THORNTREE:

Being a fence viewer. I go around seeing that people's fences are straight.

*He uses his stick to line up the children, who now pretend to
be fenceposts in a fence.*

Aye — there's where it goes crooked. It's gone crooked here, too. That post
should be a little to the — a whole sliverful of property should really be on this
side of the fence. Was that post that way before? I keep thinking of the nasty little
tricks the children played on me at the crossroads coming home from school —
and I can't think straight. All the posts are out of order. They're all dancing in a
circle around me!

*He turns on the CHORUS who make up a fence, then dissolve,
then makes up a fence again.*

Brat!

CHORUS BOY:
What?

THORNTREE:
Little girl!

CHORUS BOY:
I'm a boy!

THORNTREE:
No, you're not. You're a girl. You certainly resemble a girl. That's a girl's sweater you're wearing, anyhow. The colours are just a shade too bright for a boy's sweater.

CHORUS BOY: *dissolving and tearing off sweater*
Oh — I told Mother I wouldn't wear this sweater. Oh!

CHORUS:
Albert's a girl. Albert's a girl. Albert's a girl.

THORNTREE:
Now *you're* a boy!

CHORUS GIRL:
I am not. I'm a girl!

THORNTREE: *pause*
Kind of plain for a girl, aren't you?

CHORUS GIRL:
Oh boohoo. Boohoo.

CHORUS: *turning on her*
Mary's a boy. Mary's a boy!

THORNTREE:
Now if any of you ever get feeling cross with one of your playmates and want some assistance in making them feel punk — come to me.

CHORUS:
Caw caw caw caw
Caw caw caw caw
A crow stole Grandpa Thorntree's hat.

Raw raw raw raw
Raw raw raw raw

They snatch and play ball with the old man's battered hat.

Now, he's sorry he called me a brat
And me a girl. And me a boy.

THORNTREE:
Oh I'll never be sorry about that.
Because I'm going to get back at all kids.

CHORUS: *recovering*
Caw caw caw caw
You'll never get back at us.
You never do and you never did
Caw caw caw caw.

THORNTREE:
Do me no do's and did me no did's
I'll get my revenge on some of you kids.

CHORUS:
Haw haw haw. Old Mister Thorntree
Swallowed a peck of rusty nails
And garter snakes with wriggly tails
Spits them out and never fails
To make them twice as rusty
Twice as wriggly he makes
The snakes
And twice as rusty — the nails.

REV HACKABERRY: *enters*
Children, you should not tease Mr. Thorntree.

When last seen, HACKABERRY, too, was one of the horses.

CHORUS:
But he's so mean to us, Reverend Hackaberry.
When he is so mean we cannot be merry.

REV HACKABERRY:
But weren't you mean to him first?
And he cannot help his meanness, you know.

113

THORNTREE:

    Oh, I can't eh —

    Comes out from behind a tree — the stepladder.

    I'll get you, reverend
    I'll some evil to you send
    For sticking up for me, for trying to help me.
    I don't need your help. I don't need your charity.
    I can view fences in the summer
    And trap animals in the winter.
    And you — you're not youngsters
    You're all — moungsters and monsters!

    He chases the children.

REV HACKABERRY:

    Thorntree, you'll go too far some day
    And turn into a thorntree by the way.

THORNTREE:

    How do you know?

REV HACKABERRY:

    Look. There's a thorn sticking out of your arm already. I'll swear it grew there.

THORNTREE: *laughing it off*
    It did grow there, Hackaberry. It did grow there. And I'll tell the shrikes to put
    their victim birds on it when it's good and sharp.

REV HACKABERRY: *running after*
    Don't run away like that. Thorntree. Come back and listen to reason.

    In MRS. DELL'S kitchen.

    Last seen scattering in front of THORNTREE'S malice, the
    CHORUS now re-enter bearing dishes and kettles, and other
    kitchen utensils. One of them bears a large flashlight tied up in
    in orange cellophane to represent the setting sun. The CHORUS
    with their bodies build up a suggestion of the kitchen, mime
    windows, cupboards, doors, and so on. The CHORUS'S sunset
    song should go quite quickly — despite the slowness of real
    sunsets.

CHORUS:

      Sunset in Farmwife Dell's kitchen.

      Cups and saucers. Spoons and forks.

      Knives and plates. Tea in kettles.

      Fire in the stove. Bread in the oven.

      Plants in the windows. Wood in the woodbox.

      Towel on the roller. Water in the pail.

      Dipper in the water. Kitchen kitchen

      Supper supper. Sunset sunset.

      Sunset in Mrs. Dell's kitchen

      Sunset in Mrs. Dell's kitchen.

MRS. DELL and COUSIN ETTA enter with saucepans and dishes. They mime various kitchen tasks, using members of the CHORUS and their particular utensils.

MRS. DELL:

      Look, Etta. What a beautiful sunset. Sam and Rob should soon be in for supper.

COUSIN ETTA:

      Doesn't the sun gleam pretty on the pots and pans?

MRS. DELL:

      Etta, could you take this knife and go down into the orchard and cut some asparagus? It'll just be ready.

COUSIN ETTA:

      Why, a feed of asparagus would be wonderful for supper.

FARMER DELL: *entering with ROB*

      What you got for supper, Mrs. Dell?

MRS. DELL:

      All sorts of things, Samuel, including some asparagus fresh out of the orchard. Etta is just bringing it up.

FARMER DELL and ROB mime washing and drying themselves.

Everyone at the Dell Farm is now bedded down for a good night's sleep — a baby's crying particularly rocks the hired men. At length, morning comes. The CHORUS pretend to be chickens in the henhouse. A rooster crows and they all awaken.

115

DAWN

CHORUS:
>Occiocceroccioccer. Occioccericciocceroo.
>Time to get up. Time to get up.
>Hear about the baby? Heard about the baby?

COUSIN ETTA:
>*Enters and sprinkles feed for the chickens. Whenever she scatters it, they run and pick it up making hen cackles and any other chicken noises that come to hand.*

>Chook chook chook chook chuokk!
>Chook chook chook chook chuokk!

>Oh, Sam and Annie. What are you going to name her?

MRS. DELL:
>We thought Amelia.

COUSIN ETTA:
>And you're going off to get the Reverend Hackaberry to christen her Amelia? A beautiful name. A beautiful, beautiful name. But, oh, my dear, be careful. I saw old Grandpa Thorntree coming down the road and he looked so mean. He might say something mean about the baby or —

FARMER DELL:
>I'm not afraid of anything old Grandpa Thorntree can do.

THORNTREE: *suddenly entering*
>Out of my way, you dratted hens.

>*They all run off.*

>Trying to trip me up as usual, you stupid clucks. So you aren't afraid of me, eh, Farmer Dell? Why aren't you afraid of me?

FARMER DELL:
>I don't know, I'm just not, that's all.

COUSIN ETTA:
>You clear out of here, Grandpa Thorntree. The very look on your face would sour fresh milk in a pitcher. And you've just kicked two of my best Black Minorcas.

116

THORNTREE:

Oh, a good fat hen likes a playful kick now and then. Well, Farmer Dell and Anne Dell, what are you naming the new little baby?

COUSIN ETTA:

Don't tell him. I heard that yesterday he vowed revenge on all the children of the neighbourhood, even the ones that couldn't possibly harm or tease him.

THORNTREE:

Why that's not true, Etta dear. I've got a little present for the baby, as a matter of fact. What's its name?

MRS. DELL:

She isn't named yet. We're just taking her to be christened.

FARMER DELL:

Her name's going to be Amelia.

THORNTREE:

Oh. It's going to be Amelia, is it? Well, it isn't! I have sworn revenge on every child in the neighbourhood and my special revenge against babies is that I spoil their christening by thinking up a terrible nickname for them that will stick and stick and stick, it's so sticky. No, they won't call this baby Amelia though you may christen her that. They'll call her — what does the name Amelia — Mealy! All the children will call her that at school — Oat Mealy!

He goes off laughing and repeating the nickname. The DELLS are thunderstruck.

COUSIN ETTA:

Oh, pay no attention to him. Go ahead and have her christened anyhow. Christen her some other name.

MRS. DELL:

No, Etta. Her name has to be Amelia. But we can't christen her that until Mr. Thorntree's not around any more. And when will that be? I couldn't bear to send her off to school and have him meet her and say Mealy to her. And the other children might repeat it, too. Oh!

FARMER DELL:

What are we going to do, Annie?

MRS. DELL:

What can we do but take her back home. No christening today, poor dear.

FARMER DELL:
What else can we call her but Baby One. We'll call her that until we can christen her properly.

They go out.

THORNTREE AT THE SCHOOLYARD

CHORUS:
They come marching on. As in the first scene, they imitate these these words with bodily action. They jump across the ditch, for example.

A schoolyard a schoolyard a schoolyard
Where is the schoolyard
Where the ground is stamped hard
With the children's stamping feet
We're on the way to find it
Find it find it
On the way to school
Dew dust mud hail
Snow ice frost smoke
Road lane ditch track
    Truant officer
        Tree
        Pebble
        Water
        Splash!

The CHORUS divide up into a line of boys and a line of girls and file into school where the teacher and immediate class will be the other five chief actors seated on benches.

CHORUS:
In the School Room.

MRS. DELL:
As school marm. The kids repeat words after her and mime, or the kids could name the invisible things she points to.

Desk bell map chart
Clock book slate globe

118

Chalk paper ferrule ouch!
Blackboard children teacher printer
Student satchel pencil crayon
Register ink-bottle dictionary

ROB:

I'd like to go to school again. I never did get my Entrance. Etta, the hired girl is so cruel to me. She says I'm such an ignoramus she'd never dream of marrying me. But if I could just get my Entrance she might consider it. I wonder if the children would let me come back.

CHORUS AND
MRS. DELL: *use as much mime as possible*
What pupils do

Read write parse solve
Think reckon think learn
Think listen think attend
Study recite declaim —
Recollect and reckon compose compute
Recollect recollect recollect —
Remembrance remember remembrance
Calculate analyze

There's the Dell's hired man looking in the window!

CHORUS:

There's that old Thorntree leaning in the other window.

THORNTREE:

Listen, kids. He's too old to go back to school. And he's too dumb. Just look at him. All he knows is how to play the harmonica.

CHORUS:

Go away, Rob. You're too old.

ROB:

Then how am I to get enough education so Etta will marry me? She says I can get my Entrance if I really care to. And care for her.

CHORUS:

That's just too bad. That's your look out.

THORNTREE:

Etta's got her Entrance, Rob. Why don't you try some other girl that's not so highly

119

educated. There's Leota Throughopper down the road. She never got out of Primer Class. She'd have you. She's about your speed.

ROB:

Well — I guess that's it. I've just set my sights too high. And my eyes are turned on too low. *Exit.*

The CHORUS take over the stage now. We are in the school-yard. THORNTREE is watching.

CHORUS:

Recess   recess   Games!   games!
A schoolyard a schoolyard a schoolyard
Where the ground is hard
With the stamping children's feet.

They stamp their feet, then break into a games sequence.

Crack the Whip!
Send them flying!
Prisoner's Base

Have kids on stilts, playing tug of war, etc.

Come pull away, pull away
Bull in the ring
My bar's made of gold
My bar's made of iron
My bar's made of steel
My bar's made of stone

Have actual skipping, but watch the knots in those ropes!

Skipping skipping. The girls are skipping
   Rosy apple lemon pear
   These are the colours she should wear
The boys are walking on stilts
   I am a girl guide dressed in blue
Skipping skipping. The girls are skipping.

For the individual games and skipping rhymes, break the CHORUS up into groups.

   These are the actions I did do
   Salute the king. Turn to the queen
The boys are walking on stilts
   Turn your back on the baseball green

120

Get down you dirty rascal
    Blue bells cockleshells
    Evie ivie over
My mother said that I was born in January,
February, March, April, May, June, July, August, September
    A house to let apply within
    A woman put out for drinking gin
    I call in — *name the child*.
    All in together girls
    Very fine weather girls
    One two three four five
    Salt vinegar mustard pepper
    Cedar cider red hot pepper
Hide and go seek   Hide and go seek
    Eenie meenie minie moe
    Catch a fat one by his toe
    If he hollers let him go
    Eenie meenie minie moe
    O-U-T spells out and
    OUT you must go

A child who is "It" counts up to ten and then yells —

Anybody hiding round my gool *("Goal" is pronounced "Gool" in Southwestern*
Whether he be hidden or not   *Ontario.)*
He shall be caught
One two three on Walter!

A sulky child goes over to THORNTREE.

CHILD:
Mr. Thorntree. You said if ever we wanted to get back at somebody we might just
come to you. Well, those kids haven't let me up to bat yet — what names can I call
them?

THORNTREE:
Well — you can call 'em

Whispers.

and you can —

Whispers.

CHILD: *goes over to the CHORUS and starts a name-calling sequence*
      Hi — scummy!
      Hi — sissy!

CHORUS:
      Monkey Ape Foxy Toothy
      Fatty Warty Greasy Smelly
      Stinkpot

          Repeat ad nauseum.

          The games fade away, and the children stand about moping
          listlessly.

      I won't hold the skipping rope for her
      Not after the nicknames she's called me.
      Hey! Let's make a snowman and then smash him to bits!
      Winter isn't finished yet
      The frogs have stopped singing!

          They have invisible snowballs. But, as the snowballs fly, we still
          hear the first song.

      A schoolyard a schoolyard a schoolyard
      Where is the schoolyard
      Where the ground is stamped hard
      With the children's stamping feet
      We're on the way to find it

          Stamping.

      Find it find it
      On the way to school
      Dew dust mud hail
      Snow ice frost smoke
      Road lane ditch track
         Truant officer
            Tree
            Pebble
            Water
            Splash!

ANOTHER BABY AT THE DELLS

If one of the girls is really good at skipping, you might have a

122

If one of the girls is really good at skipping, you might have a skipping cadenza here using one of the skipping rhymes to finish the schoolyard scene with. Perhaps a fade-out to suggest that the skipping girl goes on forever. Perhaps the "January, February" skipping song should melt here into the time bridge.

CHORUS:
    Two years later in the summer
    Two years later in the summer
    Summer summer summer summer
    Another little baby was born.
    While the birds were singing

    Bird whistles of various sorts here.

    And Queen Anne's Lace was blossoming
    And ox-eyed daisy fading
    And raspberries ripening
    And honey bees humming

    Humming of bees here continues for some time.

    Beneath the golden sun
    Beneath the golden sun
    Two years later in the summer
    Summer summer summer summer
    Another babe was born — while

    Bird whistles and then bee hums.

    While while while while

    ROB and FARMER DELL enter, miming the making of hay-cocks.

ROB:
    I never thought I'd see us making this hay, it's been raining so. But the rain sloped off at last.

FARMER DELL:
    Another forkful for that coil, Rob.

ROB:
    What are you naming the new boy, Sam?

FARMER DELL:
    Well — we thought and we thought. It has to be a name that Grandpa Thorntree

can't make a horrible nickname of.

ROB:

Yessiree. There's twenty babies without names in this neighbourhood and all because of him and his terrible tongue.

FARMER DELL:

We couldn't name him Abel.

ROB:

No. You couldn't name him Abel.

FARMER DELL:

Because then Thorntree would sneer — Unable.

ROB:

Why so he would. So he would.

FARMER DELL:

We couldn't call him John. Because then old Grandpa Thorntree might call him Jack in the Pulpit or even worse — Jackass.

ROB:

It would be just like him to do that.

FARMER DELL:

So what we're going to do is have Reverend Hackaberry come over to the house at dinner time so we won't have to take the baby out onto the road to the church where we might meet old Thorntree, and we're giving the baby five names, five names so if even he hears the names, he can't possibly spoil five names all at once and we'll call the baby by the name he doesn't have time to get out.

REV HACKABERRY: *entering*
Well, Sam, what have you decided to call this baby boy of yours?

FARMER DELL:

We're going to call him Paul John Peter James Martin.

REV HACKABERRY:

Yes. That's very wise in view of the difficulty with Thorntree. Let us repair to your house then; and Rob, you might pump a pail of fresh cold water to christen this child with. Good day, Annie. Good day, Etta, and good day, Baby One.

BABY ONE should be played by a member of the CHORUS.

Enter these with a doll as the new one. BABY ONE is now a little girl. ROB mimes pumping and THORNTREE begins to climb up the stepladder or, if you like, onto the roof of the house, where he listens down the chimney. A member of the CHORUS can be a pump.

CHORUS:
Down underground it's cold as winter
Down at the bottom of the well
Pump pump pump pump
Pump pump pump pump
Up above it's fire hot summer
The sun like a golden butter nut
Pump pump pump pump
Pump pump pump pump
Pump up winter into summer
From the secret underground stream
That flows beneath us like a dream
Pump! Splash! Gurgle gurgle.
Pump pump pump pump
Gurgle gurgle gurgle gurgle

The family arrange themselves, and ROB brings in the pail of water. THORNTREE is now at the top of the stepladder.

REV HACKABERRY:
And now, Farmer Dell, what names do you give this child. This little man.

THORNTREE:
Names? I wish they'd clear their chimney better so I could hear properly. Names?

MRS. DELL:
Did you hear something on the roof?

To audience, inviting their participation.

Does anyone hear anything on the roof?

The children in the audience may tell her about THORNTREE but just as she looks, he ducks down his head.

No, I guess there isn't anybody up there.

With careful control, the audience can again be brought in here. Every time they point out THORNTREE, by the time she turns round he has ducked down. Ad lib to temperature of the occasion.

FARMER DELL:
It's the fir tree scraping against the shingles in the summer breeze. I name this child Paul.

CHORUS:
Paul.

They repeat the other names after FARMER DELL.

FARMER DELL:
John Peter James Martin

REV HACKABERRY: *taking the baby*
And now little baby I name thee —

THORNTREE:
Five names! Too many names. Fat name. Too many names. Fat name. Yah! Fat name, fat name!

He opens his umbrella and leaps off the roof.

MRS. DELL:
Oh, Sam! He was up on the roof listening to us down through the chimney. He heard the baby's names!

THORNTREE:
That makes the twenty-first child whose name I've ruined.

Laughs.

FARMER DELL:
Sic the dogs on him. Sic him, Rover. Sic him, Bluebell. Sic him, Daisy. Sic him, Rollo. Get him, Gnasher.

Members of the CHORUS leap forward.

CHORUS:
Bow wow wow! Bow wow wow!
Grr grrr grr! Grr grr grr!
Bow wow wow! Bow wow wow!
Bite him, fellow. Bite him!

They chase THORNTREE around the stage and finally off. If he goes through the audience, you're going to get audience participation, which should be carefully handled.

126

FARMER DELL:
You'd better whistle the dogs back, Rob, before he does something to them.

ROB: *whistles*
Here, Rover. Come on back. Here, Bluebell. Back you silly dogs. You're no match for Thorntree. It's no use. They won't come back for my whistle, and he's hitting them with his cane.

FARMER DELL:
We need more whistlers. Anybody here good at whistling dogs back for us?

> *The audience whistles.*

Louder and higher than that.

> *Renewed efforts. The dogs reluctantly return. Perhaps they run off, in which case the audience has to whistle them in again.*

Thatta boy, Rover. Thatta boy, Rollo.

MRS. DELL:
What will we call this baby, Sam?

FARMER DELL:
I guess we'll have to call him Baby Two.

MRS. DELL:
Baby Two. I couldn't bear to have a child called — Fat Name.

COUSIN ETTA:
I think we should get the village constable.

MRS. DELL:
Reverend Hackaberry, what are we going to do if we have another baby and cannot name it either? Nor apply for a birth certificate for them?

REV HACKABERRY:
Let us all go up to the church and pray about it. Come with me. God will surely suggest something. We'd better speak in sign language just in case there might be listeners — behind that thicket — in the ditch, underneath us in the culvert. So — speak in sign language. Now at first, Sam and Annie, you tried this —

> *He holds his hands a small space apart as in a fish story.*

Then this last time

A wider distance.

but the next time the methods we use against Grandpa Thorntree must be this —

Stretches his hands way apart, then whispers in their ears.

MRS. DELL AND
FARMER DELL:
First we tried this — *gesture*. Then we tried this — *larger gesture*. Next time try this — *biggest gesture*.

Have the gesturing and whispering repeated among the whole cast.

FARMER DELL:
It will take some study. Why, there must be hundreds of them.

MRS. DELL:
It will not only take some study but also the production of a third child. Where shall we find that?

REV HACKABERRY:
Both can be found. Meanwhile, as I see it, the problem is not to be solved this way — *the first gesture*, but only in this way — *the final gesture*. But let us go up to the church and pray.

IN THE FALL

They leave. Across the stage, the children blow like falling leaves. The main characters return to mime —

ALL:
Fall and Harvest on the farm

Rye oats	mangel-worzels
Wheat barley	turnips corn
Apple pears	geese and hogs
Chaff straw	sheaf stook
Pumpkins buckwheat	potatoes grain
Ducks drakes	chicks parsnips

Scything, turnip pulling, and stooking can be mimed here.

Crops and roots	crops and roots
Granary full	root-cellar full

128

Silo full   cellar full
Harvest, harvest   harvest, harvest
Fall, fall, fall, fall,
Autumn, autumn, autumn, autumn

> *They hum and whistle like the wind. The children whirl by*
> *again. Part of the group chant "The leaves are leaving the*
> *groves" underneath the following lines. Later on, select*
> *another repeat line and chant it under.*

Oak leaves falling, fir needles stay
Ash leaves falling, birch birch
The elms are golden and soon are bare
Beech leaves are brown and beechnuts are ripe
The leaves are leaving the groves
Under the gray sky, the bare woods and
The squirrel's asleep and the ground
Smoke from the chimney and frost on the ground.
The stream is still with
   still still
Ice Ice Ice Ice

> *The idea of things that are flowing suddenly — still — They*
> *make the wind song again and sprinkle snow from their hands.*
> *Enter THORNTREE in snowshoes. This is his moment of*
> *triumph, and the members of the CHORUS can be the*
> *various animals in his traps. Their being caught in the traps*
> *can be mimed.*

THORNTREE:
   While the other people sink in the snowy ooze
   I float above it on my snowshoes
   And everybody's afraid of me
   And everybody respects me
   While other people sink in the snowy ooze
   I float above it on my snowshoes
   Fifty unchristened babies, ha ha!
   Nameless but nicknameful
   Even the children with their names
   Dread my tongue's destroying flames
   And now I'll see what my traps are doing.

> *He bats each animal into a heap in the centre of the stage as*
> *he speaks.*

Ah! Here's a rabbit the steel is chewing
Rabbit foot not so lucky, eh?

Well stay there!
Well, what have we here ready for a box
But a full grown red-coated black-tailed fox
Get over there!
What have you caught old rusty spring?
Why, I do believe, two priceless ermine!
Get over there!
And what's in you my favourite trap?
Why, guess — a ferocious old bobcat
Get over there!
Hurray!
I'll have to go off to get my sleigh
To haul my trapped animals away
And then I'll skin them ha ha ha
And then I'll sell them — ha ha ha
While other people sink in the snowy ooze
I float above it on my snowshoes.   *Exit.*

> *Optionally, the animals put him into a frenzy by escaping from
> his traps. The stage darkens, the CHORUS rise from the heap with
> with lighted flashlights, which they move about with like the
> winter stars.*

Stars on a frosty night
In the depth of winter.
Stars on a frosty night
In the depth of winter

> *If each child has two flashlights, quite a few constellations can
> drift over the stage: the Big Dipper, Cassiopia's Chair and, last
> of all — Orion.*

Shine on the sleeping fields
Sleep beneath the snow
On the trees turned upsidedown
Their sap sunk below
Orion, Orion, Orion, Orion,
The cruel sworded giant
Made of stars he marches on
Over the snowy world.

Stars on a frosty night
In the depth of winter
Stars on a frosty night
In the depth of winter

> *A rooster crows, and it becomes light again.*

Bird whistles.

Spring on Farmer Dell's farm
The snow has melted, the snow has gone
Tra la la Tra la la Tra la la
The bare trees have put their green leaves on.
Tra la la Tra la la Tra la la
Knee deep knee deep knee deep knee deep
The frogs in the pond sing
Knee deep knee deep knee deep knee deep
The frogs in the pond sing.

> *They hum and occasionally say "knee deep" under the
> following dialogue. The CHORUS fade into less distinct
> "knee-deeps" and change into trees and fence posts along the
> road.*

THE THIRD BABY

ROB: *as if walking into town*
> Oh, dear me. I've got the time off to go in and write the examination. I shall never be able to enter the building. As to entering the room, they'll all be young kids twelve or fourteen, and here I am eighteen. I'll tower over them like a bean pole. They'll be people younger'n me writing their University Entrance, let alone the High School Entrance. I've got to quiet my mind with something — I'll see if I can kick this stone all the way into town — I never knew I had nerves till now — if I can kick it all the way into town, that means I'll pass the exam, but if I — let's see. I'll go over the Arithmetic rules in my head and then I'll do my memory work.
>
> A number that divides two or more numbers exactly is called —

> *He kicks the stone about in a circle.*

THORNTREE: *picking up the stone*
> Talking to himself. The first sign of advanced madness.

ROB:
> You give me that stone!

THORNTREE:
> Ah. A special stone, eh? You intend kicking it all the way into town and if you don't lose it, you'll pass, eh? Well — you're going to lose it. Unless —

ROB:
> Unless what?

THORNTREE:

Unless you tell me what's been going on at the Dell farmhouse lately.

ROB:

I won't tell you anything.

THORNTREE:

I'll follow you all the way into town telling people how old you are and what exam you're trying.

ROB:

I don't care.

THORNTREE:

I'll look in the window at you — I'll keep saying to myself, but you'll hear it — "Wrong, Rob, wrong, Rob."

ROB:

Oh —

THORNTREE:

I only want to know one thing, Rob. Is there a new baby at the Dell's?

ROB:

No. Not that I've heard of.

THORNTREE: *laughing*

And is it going to be christened today?

ROB:

No. It is not!

THORNTREE: *throwing back the stone*

That's all I want to know. That's all I want to know.

ROB:

Oh, you old devil.

> *Picks up the stone and rushes off.*

Now he'll ruin that baby's name too.

> *The Dell family march out of their house. FARMER DELL holding the third and latest baby. BABY ONE and BABY TWO are walking now.*

THORNTREE:

Well, Farmer Dell. So this is the latest little Dell. And all the family with you. BABY ONE and BABY TWO, I see. Hello, BABY ONE.

BABY ONE:

You are a bad man, Grandpa Thorntree.

BABY TWO:

Mooly moo dirly irly a doidle.

THORNTREE:

Yes, and where might you all be going? Off to church, perhaps?

FARMER DELL:

We're going off to church to get our children christened.

THORNTREE:

And what are you going to name them? These two's names I know — Oat Mealy, wasn't it? And Fat Name or too many names or Fatty for short. You might as well tell me what you're going to name this infant right now. So I can tell you what nickname I'll brand it with if you dare christen it.

REV HACKABERRY: *entering with a basin of water*
What names do you give these children, Samuel and Anne Dell?

> *With him enter the children, who later block off THORN-TREE'S escape.*

FARMER DELL:

This one's to be Amelia. This one's Paul John Peter James Martin and I want to name this one —

THORNTREE:

Yes, yes. Let's hear the ridiculous name so you can stop the christening party before it's too late.

FARMER DELL:

We're going to call our third boy baby

> *A drum underlines the growing river of names.*

Aaron Abel Abijah Abner
Abraham Adam Adolphus Albert
Alexander Alfred Algernon Alonzo
Alvin Ambrose Amos Andrew
Anthony Archibald Arnold Arthur
Asa Augustus

MRS. DELL:
>Baldwin Basil
>Benedict Benjamim Bernard Bertram
>Caleb Calvin Cecil Cephas
>Charles Christopher Clarence Clement
>Cornelius Cuthbert Cyril Cyrus

BABY ONE:
>Daniel David Donald

BABY TWO:
>Dionysius

ROB:

>Duncan Ebeneezer Edgar Edmund
>Edward Edwin Egbert Eli
>Elias Elijah Enoch Ephraim
>Erastus Ernest Eugene Eustace
>Ezekiel Ezra Felix Ferdinand
>Francis Franklin Frederic

ETTA:
>George
>Gideon Gilbert Godfrey Gregory

THORNTREE:
>Stop stop stop stop

ETTA:
>Gustavus Guy Harold Henry
>Herbert Herman Hezekiah Hiram
>Horace Horatio Hubert Hugh
>Humphrey Hugo Ira Isaac

FARMER DELL:
>And also Jabez Jacob James

CHORUS:
>Jasper Jerome Jesse Job
>Jobin Jonas Jonathan Joseph

THORNTREE:
>Stop stop stop stop
>I cannot stand all these names
>Names names names names

>*He sinks to the ground, then shoots up and begins to dance*

134

a thorntree dance to the names.

MRS. DELL:
       Joshua Josiah Julius Justin

CHORUS:
       Lambert Lawrence Lemuel Leonard
       Levi Lewis Lionel Lorenzo
       Lucius Luke Luther

ROB:
       Mark
       Marmaduke Matthew Maurice Martin
       Michael Miles Morgan Moses

BABY ONE:
       Nathan Nathaniel Nicholas

BABY TWO:
       Norman

ETTA:
       Octavius Oliver Orlando Oscar

CHORUS:
       Patrick Paul Peleg Peter
       Philip Phineas oh — oh

They hum as everyone gathers up speed.

FARMER DELL:
       Ralph Raphael Raymond Reginald Reuben

CHORUS:
       Richard Robert Roderic Roger Roland

MRS. DELL:
       Rufus Rupert Samson Samuel Saul

CHORUS:
       Seth Silas Silvanus Silvester Simeon

FARMER DELL:
       Simon Solomon Stephen Sydney Thaddeus

CHORUS:
       Theodore!

FARMER DELL:
>Theophilus Thomas Timothy Urban

CHORUS:
>Vincent!

FARMER DELL:
>Walter Zachariah!

>*By this time, THORNTREE has danced himself off the stage.*

REV HACKABBERY:
>Quick, Rob. Go and see what's happened to the old trapper. I thought I saw him fall down there.

FARMER DELL:
>It worked. We named Old Grandpa Thorntree so many names he couldn't think of a nickname. Couldn't think of anything towards the last there but just to get away.

ROB: *bringing in a dead thorntree*
>Well, look what's happened to him. He's changed into a thorntree, at least I think he has.

ETTA:
>That's his hat, and there's his cane.

MRS. DELL:
>How did he do that?

REV HACKABERRY:
>He was so balked, his envy and spite were so frustrated, that they turned in upon themselves and produced this awful miracle.

BABY ONE:
>Poor old Grandpa Thorntree.

MRS. DELL:
>Don't you dare touch that dead tree, Amelia. It might still hurt you! Amelia—
>I can call her by her rightful name. And Paul. Little Paul, I can call you by your name now. And which of his hundred names will we call this little dear?

FARMER DELL:
>Whichever the first name I said was.

MRS. DELL:
>Aaron. Little Aaron who struck the rock and forth came water.

REV HACKABERRY:

Think of all the other babies who can now be properly christened.

ETTA:

But now we must go home and have enough christening dinner for three little christened ones. But where were you this afternoon, Rob? We missed you.

ROB:

I was to town. Etta, do you see this stone?

ETTA:

I certainly do. Is there anything extra-special about it?

ROB:

When I was walking into town today to write my examination, I said to myself, "If I can kick this stone all the way into town and back, I'll probably pass." And I did. And you know how hard that is.

ETTA:

Yes, Rob.

ROB:

If it turns out I did pass the Entrance examination, will you marry me?

ETTA:

Rob, I've been thinking. I'll marry you whether you pass it or not. Now that Grandpa Thorntree is gone, it's safe to get married and have babies with proper names again. That's really what was troubling me.

MRS. DELL:

So we must make this a betrothal party as well as a christening party. What will we eat at this party?

The words are arranged in a "Turkey in the Straw" pattern which the six main actors dance while the CHORUS chant. A dance of girls with dolls is a possibility here, since all the young children in the district can now be properly christened.

CHORUS:

Oh — buns and rolls, soups and teas
Sauces and pies, sauces and pies
Stews and muffins, biscuits waffles
Butter and pastries, porridge and milk
Pancakes and crackers, doughnuts, dumplings
Pancakes and crackers, doughnuts, dumplings
Blanc mange puddings sandwiches cocoa
And other good things to eat, to eat.

Everyone laughs.   Then — switch the mood to —

Vale hill dell dale
Path road ditch post
Barn shed tree house
Long ago   long ago   on
Farmer Dell's Farm.

Ignoramus

A Note for Ignoramus

Some time ago over CBC Wednesday Night I remember hearing a wonderful debate between Dr. Hilda Neatby and somebody else about her book, *So Little For the Mind.* The controversy about educational theory that arose from this book in the early fifties brought out tensions and groupings still visible, no matter how changed.

More or less as a tribute to that debate I have written the following play. I have always wanted to try an Aristophanes Old-Comedy type of play where you have lots of comic chorus work and grotesque farcical combats. Also, this is a companion play to *Names and Nicknames:* there I used an old public-school text — *The Practical Speller;* here I have used *Cours Moyen* and other high-school texts so that it can easily be a play for young people with their teachers taking the adult roles, all working together at interpretation and precision. I hope the play is amusing, but I also hope that if you saw the Roman Empire as a chant-dance-mime in front of you, you might then take away the attitude that history was fun, not just labour. Similarly with the grammar scene and the chemistry sequence. A whole school and all its curricular and extra-curricular activities can be involved. One production used the swimming team as the twenty orphan babes wheeled from the back of the cafeteria in shopping carts. The only caution with expansion of the script is that the pace and line of the play *must* be kept; there's no point in doing the chemistry, French or geometry sequences unless you can make them funny or dazzling or weird, but *always* part of the line forward. Bon Ami cans have changed, by the way. Find out from parents what they used to be like.

Ignoramus was first performed at York Mills Collegiate Institute in Toronto, Ontario, in February, 1967, with the following cast:

Newsboy	David Marmorek
Announcer	Elliot Strom
Voices	Janet Goforth
Governor-General	Gordon Gates
Mr. Frothingale	John Porter
Dr. Hilda History	Brigitte Berman
Dr. Charles Progessaurus	Andy Stoddart, Graham Mackey
Beatrice	Taraneh Harari, Martha Meschino
Bruce	Scott McGill
Cynthia	Pam Wiggin, Heather Gold
Stephen	Dean Samaris, Tony Hall
Dr. Hilda's Pupils	Barbara Taylor, Marina Strauss
	Chris Schoeck, Gordon Thompson
	Judy Libman, David Marmorek
Dr. Charles' Pupils	Helen Gibson, Sandra Feldman
	Bob Dolman, Jeff Gold
	Miriam Gotlib, Florence Minz
	Carol Duncan
Cheerleaders	Helen Meschino, Phil Holzberg
	Penny Tibbles, Carolyn Brown
	Bev Read, Jay Bigelow
Nurses and Babies	Wendy Clare, Jack Pasht
	Gail Stover, Dave Patterson
	Bill Pepali, Debbie Brooker
	Debbie Pemberton, Mark Shriver
	Sandy Imrie, Graham Clow
	Sue Fitzgerald, Charlie Lumbers
	Joyce Beaupre, Dave Shalof
	Pat Mackie, George Goldsmith
	Janet Goldring, John Baird
	Penny Luke, Bruce Grantier
	Johanne Clare, Tris Organ

Directed by Doug Dales
with the assistance of Mr. D. Daniels and Mr. R. Lawrason
Produced by Mr. D. Mogan with Howard Greenspan and Kirk Hewitt
Costumes under the direction of Mrs. Don Lang
Music under the direction of Mr. Patterson

CHARACTERS

NEWSBOY

ANNOUNCER

HILDA HISTORY

DR. PROGRESSAURUS

FIRST VOICE FROM AUDIENCE

SECOND VOICE FROM AUDIENCE

MR. FROTHINGALE	a brewer
CHILDREN AT MISS HISTORY'S SCHOOL	Alfred, Jerry, Bruno, Stephen, Cynthia, Mary, Samuel, David, and others
CHILDREN AT DR. PROGRESSAURUS' SCHOOL	Beatrice, Ralph, Mildred, Bruce, Bob and others

GOVERNOR GENERAL

A bare fully lit uncurtained stage. A semicircle of chairs — a janitor's broom leaning against a chair. Darting up the aisle comes a screaming NEWSPAPER BOY yelling the latest head-line:

TWENTY ORPHANS AGED TWENTY MONTHS MADE HOMELESS BY FLOOD READ ALL ABOUT IT ORPHANAGE COLLAPSES. TWENTY INFANT ORPH-ANS HOMELESS ON THE STREETS!

As his voice dies away, up on the stage file the actors in the play. Generally speaking there will be four actors for adult parts, and twenty for the students. But all the actors should be prepared to fill in where necessary. That is, if nurses are needed for the school sequence, let someone don a nurse's blue cloak.

MARVIN MELLOWBELL, Rawhide's announcer, picks up
the janitor's broom which has CBC pinned on it and so we
have a radio broadcast. Perhaps a box can be placed in front
of him and two LISTENERS crouch at it, twiddling with knobs
knobs, adjusting their rocking chairs as he says:

ANNOUNCER:

Good evening, ladies and gentlemen. This evening Citizens Forum brings you a debate between *pause* DR. HILDA HISTORY who has just written a controversial book *pause* *So Little For the Spine* — a debate between DR. HILDA HISTORY and, on the other hand, DR. CHARLES PROGRESSAURUS, B.A., M.A. Toronto, B. Paed. Toronto, D. Paed Columb., principal of Toronto's famed centre for Tomorrow's Education. DR. PROGRESSAURUS. Perhaps there are a few questions you would like to ask DR. HILDA HISTORY about her recent book *So Little For the Spine.* Now, some commentators have stated that it made the most crushing indictment possible of Centre for Tomorrow's Education and all progressive education.

PROGRESSAURUS:

It — *So Little For the Spine* — tried to make a crushing statement.

HISTORY:

It indicted and it crushed.

HISTORY AND
PROGRESSAURUS:

Crush and Crunch
Gentle press
Crush!   *They repeat these words until they*
Press!   *become "Cress" and "Pruch."*

PROGRESSAURUS:

Awgyh! You have written the most old-fashioned book. In which you say. That progressive education. Does not train the child's mind for anything.

HISTORY:

Right!

PROGRESSAURUS:

Ho ho ho! What's the use of training and straining and stuffing the child's mind with a lot of facts he'll never use. At Centre for Tomorrow's Education we believe in teaching the whole child to be happy, teaching him to fit into his environment — our great happy democracy.

HISTORY:

Define your terms! What do you mean by democracy?

PROGRESSAURUS:

I uh uh er would rather not say. With your very clever debating type mind you'd just — jump me.

HISTORY:

Oh ha! So you can't define, can't or won't define democracy and yet you're training the child to fit in with some great happy form of it. Dr. Progressaurus. Do you know what you're like?

PROGRESSAURUS: *fascinated*

No. What am I like?

HISTORY:

You're like a man hammering a nail in the dark.

PROGRESSAURUS:

I suppose you believe in stuffing their minds with dates and figures and rules and theorems and — LATIN. Greek and LATIN.

HISTORY:

You're giving them something to think about. Latin trains the mind. LATIN.

PROGRESSAURUS:

Latin
Is
Coffin Satin
Lining
So far as I'm concerned.

What I believe is that the child should be taught to express himself — just a moment, please let me finish, let me finish, to express himself and to be happy in his environment.

HISTORY:

First of all: How can a child express himself if he's got nothing to express?

PROGRESSAURUS:

The self. Teach him to free the beautiful self!

HISTORY:

Perhaps he won't want to be happy in this society. Perhaps he'll decide that it's

149

an evil society.

PROGRESSAURUS:

Oh he'll never say that about our free happy car-driving democracy.

HISTORY:

GRAMMAR helps one to speak!

PROGRESSAURUS:

BARE SUBJECT, BARE Slimubject.

No child should be forced to learn what he doesn't want to learn.

HISTORY:

But how does he know that he doesn't want to until he's learned it?

PROGRESSAURUS:

It's too late then.

HISTORY:

Well, a little learning may be a dangerous thing, Dr. Progressaurus, but no learning at all should certainly be even more lethal.

PROGRESSAURUS:

You're not democratic.

HISTORY:

The mind is a kingdom. Surely the best democracies had lots of trained minds.

PROGRESSAURUS:

Aw — a telephone directory trains the mind. Driving a car trains the mind.

HISTORY:

With another five years of you around this country's schools our children will soon be able to read only traffic signals.

PROGRESSAURUS:

You are rather conventional in your views, but I think you will soon realize that you are attacking a good thing. Have you ever thought of the helpless misery your system inflicts on a child who can't parse a sentence or solve a problem in mathematics.

HISTORY:

Booh Hoo!

ANNOUNCER:

> Ah — a question from the floor.

VOICE: *from audience*

> I should like to ask Dr. History where she got the information for her book on modern education in the schools of tomorrow.

HISTORY:

> My dear, the various provincial departments of education put out statements of what they're trying to do. It's usually what he says — train the child to fit in with our happy democracy and learn how to express himself. I beg your pardon?

VOICE:

> Uh — I was just going to add that I am a teacher and I never pay any attention to the curriculum the department sends out.

HISTORY:

> Good! I'm glad to hear it.

VOICE II:

> I would like to ask Dr. Progressaurus if there isn't a problem about this fitting people into an environment.

PROGRESSAURUS:

> My good man, what is your little problem?

VOICE II:

> Suppose your environment's evil?

PROGRESSAURUS: *sputtering*

> But — you uh uh. In short, you believe the child is ignorant and imperfect and needs cultivation with dead language and so-called mental discipline?

HISTORY:

> Yes. In short, you believe that the child is perfect and all his teacher should do is let him do what he likes. Good gracious me, that's how the Nazis trained their very best SS men. Just let them express themselves and Original Sin will do the rest! FIGHT!

> *They fence with huge cardboard swords.*

STUDENTS: *on stage, taking sides and shouting*

> Truth   Beauty   KILL HIM!

SELF	EX!	PRESSION!
PLATO	ROUSSEAU	ARISTOTLE
GENESIS	ABEL	CAIN!

HILDA wins the fencing match just as the ANNOUNCER
rings the bell.

ANNOUNCER:
This is CBC's Citizens Forum. In just ten seconds we'll give you the second round of the debate between Traditional and Modern, Old Fashioned and Progressive E-du-cation.

GROUP:
Dr. Hilda History said:

HISTORY:
I choose as my weapon — readers! Let us fight with readers, Dr. Progressaurus. Name the reader you would present to the infant unable to read.

GROUP:
Dr. Progressaurus replied:

PROGRESSAURUS:
Dick, Jane and Puff. You name your reader.

GROUP:
Dr. Hilda History replied:

HISTORY:
My primer reader for the infant Canadian shall be called — Julius Caesar, Cleopatra and Hannibal's Elephants.

GROUP:
Dr. Progressaurus countered — rather weakly.

PROGRESSAURUS:
Well, I think that a little first book for a first little mind should have a little tittle — er I mean, a little title: Mary, John and Peter?

GROUP:
To which Dr. Hilda History said:

152

HISTORY:

My first reader is called:
Eloise, Vercingetorix and *Saint* Peter.

GROUP:

BUT said Progressaurus:

PROGRESSAURUS:

You can't have a child's first reader called — that.

HISTORY:

Well, you can!

GROUP:

She said she could!

HISTORY:

It's a duel to the death, Progressaurus. Let's throw our readers at each other.

There is some sort of "discus-throwing" here with empty boxes made to look like books. HILDA'S reader knocks PROGRESSAURUS over.

GROUP:

She did. He did. Hers was so heavy, it knocked him down.
And the citizens cheered.
Hurrah for Grammar, Arithmetic, Logic.
Down with Self-Expression!

Confetti and streamers are thrown at HILDA HISTORY who stands with her reader over the prostrate form of DR. PRO-GRESSAURUS. But now enters, or rather comes upon stage, that wealthy brewer — MR. FROTHINGALE.

FROTHINGALE:

Excuse me. But, Dr. History and Dr. Progressaurus, I've enjoyed this Citizens Forum very much and I wondered if there was anything I could do to help.

HISTORY:

The Lord hath delivered mine enemy into my hands. What need I your help, merchant?

FROTHINGALE:

To find out. If you're right. On the right track, you know. You see I've simply pots —

153

really barrels of money to give away and nobody, nobody will take it.

HISTORY:

Goodness gracious me. Why won't they, sir. Is your money tainted in some way?

FROTHINGALE:

The colleges won't touch it because I simply asked that they call one of the buildings I gave them Frothingale Hall. As you may know I'm a very wealthy brewer.

HISTORY:

Poor little rich brewer, eh? I'm afraid, my dear fellow, I still don't see how you can help us.

FROTHINGALE:

Well. I just happen to have adopted twenty orphans. Suppose, let us suppose, that with my millions of hiccup money I were to build you each a school — a small village even, in some remote part of the country, and you each with ten children a-piece were to find out over a period of say seventeen years — were to find out just what happens when you Dr. Hilda History bring up kids according to your traditional methods and you Dr. Progressaurus use your progressive theories on your ten little younkers.

PROGRESSAURUS: *rising*

I'll win this debate yet. You'll see — give me a chance to educate the whole child and in seventeen years I'll turn out paragons!

HISTORY:

Where are the infants? I'm game, Frothingale.

FROTHINGALE:

I've got them just outside. Earlier this evening their orphanage was flooded out and poor little dears, I took them in at the Frothingale Brewery. But do wait. There is a catch. At the end of the seventeen-year period — Grade Twelve, or Middle School, as it used to be called in my very old-fashioned youth, — then we will meet again and a judge chosen by me will decide — which one of you wins. I'll have him see your children — why they'll be almost grown up then.

HISTORY:

What do the children get out of this? Besides our experimenting with them. By the way, Frothingale, you must somehow arrange that they have foster parents immediately. I don't want them to grow up thinking *I'm* their mother.

FROTHINGALE:

I'll arrange that. When they are seventeen the children will get further board and

154

tuition at whatever they want right up to the Ph.D. But the group that wins will inherit — the Frothingale Brewery, and I might say that that means a great deal of hiccup money. I have no children. My wealth embarrasses me. Forge me a society of human beings who will know what to do with my money when I'm gone.

HISTORY AND
PROGRESSAURUS:
Bring forth the orphans!

> *The GROUP who have retired now come on wheeling empty*
> *baby carriages. The students are both nurses and babies.*
> *They gurgle, coo and cry and then reach forward to comfort.*
> *Let the image register of twenty orphan babies THEN!*

PROGRESSAURUS:
Are we allowed to choose our ten babies? Hey, Dr. History, stop. She's picking out the pippins. I'll have this one. Heavens! Look what a temper it has. Why it's getting redder and redder in the face. Perhaps I'd — he looks like a smart little duffer — Ughhh! He bit my finger!

FROTHINGALE:
No. You are neither of you allowed to choose. If you'll notice there is a number on each carriage, duplicated, by a number in a medallion linked around each little dimpled wrist — you must close your eyes and choose the numbers from — my hat.

> *He shuffles the hat and then presents it to the two doctors.*

HISTORY:
Ah 9! Oh goodness me, number 7. The one that found your finger so tasty, Progressaurus.

PROGRESSAURUS:
Ah 12. Look at those eyes. Good Heavens! Hasn't he rather a lot of teeth for two months?

FROTHINGALE:
Tomorrow you will each take your ten infants to opposite ends of Canada. You, Dr. Progressaurus, on an island in Lake Erie where arrangements will be made. You, Dr. History, in a remote prairie village where arrangements will be made. Tell me what you want. Your wish is my command.

HISTORY:
Nurses! Babies 9, 7, 2, 5, 11, 13, 15, 16, 18, 20 are to be put to bed this very minute. I suggest a two o'clock feeding which I will personally prepare. Number two here is

sucking his little big toe. I don't think that is a good thing. Suppose we paint it with ipecacuanha. Then *they fade off* the little dear will get the idea.

PROGRESSAURUS:

Well, Nurse. What do babies feel like doing at this hour of night? Do you want to go to sleep? Or stay up and play?

One babe, as his ten are wheeled out and he follows, utters a blood curdling baby shriek!

The wise old brewer advances towards us and confides:

FROTHINGALE:

And so, near Dauphin, Manitoba, Dr. Hilda History reared her brood of ten.
And so, on Pelee Island, in Lake Erie, Dr. Progressaurus reared his brood of ten.

You must imagine now that six years pass and the earth turning and turning we come to Dr. Hilda History's classroom first, though of course I only heard of this many years later.

Perhaps he stands at edge of stage whirling a globe and looking on.

Dr. History enters with her little scholars. They sit in a circle and hear the end of the fairy tale "Rapunzel."

CHILD:

Please Miss History, I'm afraid of the dark at night. What can I do about being afraid of the dark?

HISTORY:

Be afraid of it. If you're afraid of it now you won't be afraid of it later.

CHILD:

Should we be afraid of the dark?

HISTORY:

Yes. The dark *is* frightening. I'm still afraid of it, somewhat. But, child, once you see that it is frightening, then it's no longer quite so frightening, is it?

CHILD:

My father says you shouldn't read us stories about big giant people like Hercules.

156

HISTORY:

And why not, if I may ask.

CHILD:

He says it will give me an inferiority complex.

HISTORY:

You tell your father, child, that at this stage you should have an inferiority complex. Will you tell him that?

CHILD:

Yes, Miss History. Miss History, my mother told me last night in the village that we had not always lived here, but come from ever so many miles away all as babies on the train.

HISTORY:

Yes. I think everyone in the village remembers that night. In good time I will tell you why we are here.

CHILD:

Are you God, Miss History?

HISTORY:

No, dear. I'm not.

CHILD:

That's what the people in the village call you.

HISTORY:

Yes, that fact has percolated through to me.

CHILD:

Are you our real mother, Miss History?

HISTORY:

My dear child, no. Ah, those fingernails are clean today. Now you may put away your embroidery girls, and boys, be careful of your needle when folding up your darning.

CHILD:

Miss History, who are our real fathers and mothers?

HISTORY:

We can never know, dear. But your foster mothers and foster fathers in the village love you just as dearly. Why the stars are coming out and it's only four o'clock in the afternoon. I must say we were sent to a village sufficiently remote. Put on your overshoes and we'll race back to the village. See how many constellations you can name.

They mime putting on overshoes and the journey into the village. Perhaps they carry flashlights.

Cassiopoia's Chair	The Dipper	The Pleiades
The Hare	Orion	Perseus
Pegasus	Ursa Major	Ursa Minor
	The Dragon	

HISTORY:

Excellent. Now see how many individual stars you can call by name.

CHILD:

Oh look, Miss History. There's the lights of the village. Don't they look like stars?

*PROGRESSAURUS comes on with his brood. He is just finishing up the story of "The Little Blue Engine." " — he thought he could. He thought he could. And so the milk, the toys, the apples and the oranges **did** get to the good little boys and girls on the other side of the mountain."*

BEATRICE:

Dr. Progressaurus, could you tell us a fairy tale?

PROGRESSAURUS:

Tell you a what? Wherever did you hear about fairy tales?

CHILD:

The nurse told Alice one last night when she couldn't sleep. It was lovely. All about a girl who had hair so long it could be used for a ladder.

PROGRESSAURUS:

Beatrice, don't you see the harm it might do you? Why all sorts of dreadful things happen in that story that would — oh just unsettle your little mind. You might get an inferiority complex and want your hair to be long, long, long.

BEATRICE:

But we're not jealous of the little blue engine.

158

PROGRESSAURUS:

All right. I'll change the part where the rusty old engine can't get over the mountain. I didn't know you saw yourself that way.

BEATRICE:

But Dr. Progressaurus I *want* you to tell me a fairy tale.

PROGRESSAURUS:

You can't truly want that, dear. Let's put it to a vote then.

BEATRICE:

No, no, no. Please don't, Dr. Progressaurus.

PROGRESSAURUS:

Why don't you call me by my first name, Beatrice? Eh? If I told you a fairy tale it would ruin your vocabularies. You all know exactly one hundred words. And I'd have to do a word-count on a fairy tale before I could read it to you. Now, kids, now that our story's over, let us do some finger-painting.

They mime this.

CHILD:

Hey, Charley. I'm afraid of the dark at night.

PROGRESSAURUS:

Ask Nursey to leave your light on, Ralph.

CHILD:

Charley, why am I afraid of the dark?

PROGRESSAURUS:

It's a complex you've got, kid. But there's a nice old man coming here on Friday night and he'll find out why you're afraid of the dark.

BEATRICE:

Isn't he afraid of the dark because it's dark?

PROGRESSAURUS:

Beatrice. Get your hands into the paint more, dear. Why golly, little man, don't you want to finger-paint?

CHILD: *razzberrying*

Nah. I hates finger-painting.

159

PROGRESSAURUS: *taking notes*
But all the other kiddies are loving their finger-painting.

CHILD:
Nah. I hates it, Charley. I don't want to.

PROGRESSAURUS:
Well, Jerry. *Don't* you finger-paint. Don't you let me see you finger-painting ever again.

> *The CHILD immediately digs into the paint pot and mimes a slather.*

> *PROGRESSAURUS smiles benignly and passes on to the next child. Picks up a small blanket.*

I say, Mildred. What is this blanket you're always carrying around?

CHILD:
It's my beddie. Don't you dare touch it.

PROGRESSAURUS:
My dear little girl, all the other children don't have to have their beddy blankets with them.

CHILD:
Well, I do. And you leave it alone, Charles.

BEATRICE:
You have your pipe, Dr. Progressaurus. If you're going to ask that Mildred give up her beddy then you should give up your old pipe.

PROGRESSAURUS:
Mildred doesn't have to give it up, Beatrice. Golly, for a six-year-old girl you're — a regular caution. Now, kids. If you like, go over and wash your hands and then lie down on your mattresses for the resting time.

> *They mime washing up, splashing and lying down.*

BEATRICE: *drying hands*
Dr. Progressaurus. Why do we live in a place that's all alone except for you and the nurses? Have we always been here?

160

PROGRESSAURUS:

No. You're part of a wonderful experiment, Beatrice.

BEATRICE:

You're not our father, then?

PROGRESSAURUS:

No, dear.

BEATRICE:

I didn't think you were. The kids were all talking about this yesterday and some of them said the big tulip tree at the end of the garden was our father. You know the tree where the eagles nest?

PROGRESSAURUS:

No. I don't know. Now — if you like, *all* rest. Down on your matsies.

Eventually they subside.

I'll be down by the beach children if you need me. Smoking my beddy.

BEATRICE: *rousing the sleeping forms*
Come on, kids. I've got great news.

CHILDREN:

What?!

BEATRICE:

I've been learning how to read.

CHILD:

Oh don't, Beatrice. Charley says you'll go blind. Your eye-muscles aren't ready yet.

BEATRICE:

I don't care. The farmer's wife taught me. They throw all their old tin cans across the fence into the school property in the woods. And I asked her if I could have one of the old tin cans with pictures on it and she said, "Sure. I'll even read you what's written on it."

CHILD:

Here comes Charley back.

BEATRICE:

She flourishes an empty can of Bon Ami cleaning powder.

161

Come on, let's go up to the attic. And I'll read it to you. It's all about this little chicken. See him? He's just hatched out of the egg and he hasn't scratched yet.

They race off.

HILDA'S class run in with a long piece of rope.

HISTORY:

Now children, what do you call this rope?

CHILDREN:

We call this rope time. All of time.

HISTORY:

All that we know of time. Very well. Today, children, we are going to decorate this rope. And I've given you each little bits of coloured thread which I want you to tie on at certain places. Tie a red ribbon where B.C. ends, Jacob. That's right. Now tie a purple thread where Socrates is killed, Mary. A little closer to Jacob's thread, dear. Now, Samuel, tie your orange thread at the point where many people think man first appeared on earth. Right! And now, Bruno, tie your white thread for the end of the Azoic period. Good. Alfred, tie a thread where the provinces of Canada are confederated. Good. Now David, tie your thread where Byzantium falls to the Turks in 1453. So — now — lift up the time rope. Children, do you see what a great deal of space is here before man arrives on the scene?

CHILD:

The dinosaurs were instead of us.

Are we really descended from dinosaurs, Miss History?

HISTORY:

I once met a man who I'm quite sure was. But the greater danger is that we're turning into dinosaurs. Very well. Let us break off. You may talk and play for five minutes.

She retires and examines the globe, spinning it, while the children chatter and skip with the time-rope.

HISTORY: *returning*

What I wish we could do with time. Now for the rest of our history lesson. Let us now do: KINGS AND EMPERORS.

CHILD:

Please, Hilda, can we do the Roman Empire?

162

HISTORY:

Come here, my child

Smacks her on the hand.

let that be a lesson to you never to call me by my first name.

CHILD:

Ow! Oh dear, I'm awfully sorry, Miss History. But could we do the Roman Empire?

HISTORY:

Wouldn't you rather do the Chinese Empire?

ALL:

Ming! Chang! Ping!

CHILD:

No, we wanta do

ALL:

THE DECLINE AND FALL OF THE ROMAN EMPIRE

OR

A LESSON FROM HISTORY IN HISTORY

This sequence needs further research and explanation, preferably by the Classics teacher and his/her students. The pronunciation and spelling alone might take a day to check out. Think up mimes that fit the most prominent names, for example, the Wolf who suckled Romulus and Remus can be made out of a gymnastic combination of three bodies. Use small-sized actors for the ancestral sucklers. As long as the rhythm of the play is not lost, there is a great deal of interpretation and improvisation possible here with big moments at assassinations and poisonings; diminuendoes towards the fall.

Romulus!   Romulus   et Remus   et Lupa

Titus Tatius   Numa Pompilius   Tarquinius Priscus

                            Tarquin!

Res   Publica   Senatus   Populusque

                    ROMAE

Hannibal   Scipio   Publius   Cornelius

Sulla   Latifundi   Minifundi   Gracchi!

Marius   Pompey   Cicero   and Caesar

Julius Caesar!   Julius Caesar!   Julius — Brutus!

              Antony et Cleopatra!

              AUGUSTUS

Augustus   Tiberius   Caligula   Claudius!

Nero   Vespasian   Titus   Domitian!

Nerva   Trajan   Termini   Termini

Termini   termini   termini   termini   TERMINI

Hadrian   Antoninus   Pius   Marcus   Aurelius

Unum   centem   sexegesima unum

Gloria   glorissima   gloria   glorissimus!

Commodus Septimus   Severus   Alexander

Caracalla   Macrinus   Elogabalus

Max iminus   Pupienus   et Balbinus

              Philip the Arab!

Decius   Gallus   Aemilianus and Valerian

Gallienus   Claudius   Quintillus et Aurelian

Tacitus   Probus   Carus   Carinus   et Numerian

Diocletian   Constantius

                    CONSTANTINE

Julian   Jovian   Valentinian   Honorius

                    Valenteninian
                    the Third

Maximus   Avitus   Majorian   Severus

Anthemus   Olybrius   Glycerius   Julius Negros

                    ROMULUS

                    Romulus

                Romulus Augustulus

            Sic transit gloria Romae/Romulus

            Romulus! Romulus et Remus et Lupa!

They leave and PROGRESSAURUS comes on with his geo-
graphy lesson.

PROGRESSAURUS: *with a red flag*
Now today, children, we are going to have our first lesson in what is called Social
Studies.

BEATRICE:
Excuse me, Dr. Progressaurus, but didn't that used to be called History and Geography?

PROGRESSAURUS:
Beatrice. In social studies we learn about lands and we learn about the people who
live in those lands. Now I want the girls to take the sand on the beach here and
make it into a heap so that you have a ditch that goes in a circle. We are going to
make a model of a kind of land that many people live in. Boys, go down to the
water and fill your sand pails with water.

BOY:
I don't want to.

PROGRESSAURUS:
Raise your hands all those who want to continue with the lesson.

All do except the boy.

You must go along with the majority, Bruce. That is what we call a democracy.

BOY:
I still don't want to.

PROGRESSAURUS:
Why, Bruce?

BOY:

Because I don't.

PROGRESSAURUS:
Then you'll feel awfully alone, Bruce. Good girls. Just a lovely heap of sand. Now — pour in the water, boys.

BEATRICE:
Oh, I know. This is a lesson about land forms. We're going to find out what —

PROGRESSAURUS: *clapping a hand over her mouth*
Please Beatrice. I want the class to find out for themselves. You're always ruining lessons this way. You'll tell them what it is before they find out what it is. So I'll just have to put this bandage around your mouth.

He gags her.

Now children. Is the heap of sand the girls made completely surrounded by the water the boys brought in their pails?

ALL:
Yes.

PROGRESSAURUS:
Very well then. Now, we're going off on a walk by the water. We'll always keep by the water and I'll put this small red flag in the sand here. Yes — we won't need the model we made, Bruce. We've got a much larger model. *Chuckle.* You do quite right to kick the heap of sand the girls made — we've got a much, much larger model.

By the way, how many of you think we'll see the red flag again if we keep walking in one direction along the water?

ALL: *some shake heads, others say yes*
"No. We'll never see it again. Yes! We will."

> *BEATRICE goes into a mute frenzy of sign language.*

PROGRESSAURUS:

Now we'll just find out, shall we? Oh golly, this is going to be a perfect lesson. I'll write it up and send it in for possible publication to the *Teacher of Tomorrow Magazine.* Goodbye, little red flag.

ALL:

Goodbye, little red flag.

> *As they go off, noise diminishes. But BRUCE darts back to take the flag.*
>
> *Now the noise crescendoes as they come round the island and enter again on opposite side of stage.*

PROGRESSAURUS:

Now kids — here's — well, I guess that little red flag is just a bit further on than I thought.

> *Furious gestures from BEATRICE.*

Yes, I know — but I don't think that is the heap of sand we made with the — water — Bruce would go and kick it, of course — I'm not blaming you Bruce. You should follow your natural playful instincts. Come on, kids, we'll find that flag yet.

BRUCE:

Charley. How can we find the flag if we keep on walking away from it?

PROGRESSAURUS:

That's a very good question, Bob. But you see I've a hunch that there's some way this piece of land we live in will bring us — after a while — closer again to the little red flag we left behind us. Come on, kids. Let's keep on walking.

> *BRUCE now puts up the flag again and BEATRICE sees him.*

No, Beatrice. You may not take your mouth gag off.

> *Fade out. Just as their noise fades in again BRUCE gallops in and cabbages the flag. BEATRICE fights him for it, but he wins and puts the flag behind him.*

167

PROGRESSAURUS:

Well, kids, this i-oops is bigger than I thought. We'll just have to keep on. Say, Beatrice. What are you trying to tell me? By golly — Bruce. You picked up the flag and you put it in your pocket. That was very aggressive, Bruce, and shows hostility. Well — put the flag down, Bruce. So we walked and walked along the water and we came back to where we started from. What do we call that, I wonder?

ALL:

The land where we live.

BRUCE:

Charley. We've walked all the way round a lake.

PROGRESSAURUS:

No, Bruce. We didn't.

BRUCE:

Well we could reach the flag again if we walked around a lake.

PROGRESSAURUS:

We're in a lake but —

BRUCE:

You see —

PROGRESSAURUS:

Well — leave that flag there and we'll just walk around the beach once more. Come on.

A Marx brothers' routine. Shouts of:

The water completely surrounds us! It's a lake. We just run around a lake! Hands up! How many believe in me rather than Bruce?

Hands go up.

BRUCE:

The majority believe in me, Charley.

PROGRESSAURUS:

All right, Beatrice. Take off your gag and vote!

She raises her hand.

BRUCE:

It's still a draw!

BEATRICE:

No, it is not. We live on an island. An island is a piece of land completely surrounded by water.

BRUCE:

Prove it!

BEATRICE:

I can't prove this place is an island if you won't believe that it is. You still think the world is flat.

BRUCE:

All right. Now how many think we live on an island?

All raise hands. Eventually, even BRUCE.

PROGRESSAURUS:

Isn't this wonderful. This is the way a democracy should work. Now it's time, kids, for your "do what you like" break. Thank you Beatrice. You brought in the word "island" at just the right moment.

They fade off.

LANGUAGES

PROGRESSAURUS' GROUP:

See page 309 of Cours Moyen.

In this sequence, have a French teacher fill in the correct phonetic symbols, as well as the proper accents, and rehearse the group. Play with the sounds.

$(\ i\ )$!   ici, ile, bicyclette

$(\ e\ )$!   ecole, donner, allez

$(\ \ \ )$!   tete, merci, neige, avec

i i i i i

e e e e e

(a) !   madame!

(a) !   pas! passer

(   ) !   joli restaurant!

(o)   jour ou

      a   o u u!

u u u u u!

(Y) !   rue

(   ) !   bleu

(oe) !   oeuf

(c) !   ce

œ œ œ œ œ œ

LANGUAGES II

HISTORY'S GROUP: *rapidly*

    Nouns!

    First Declension!

    Singular

    Nominative   porta

Accusative					portam!
Genitive					portae
Dative					portae
Ablative					porta
Vocative					porta

Plural!

Portae	portas	partarum	portis	portis	portae!

Verbs!

VOCO!

Passive!	Imperfect!	Indicative!
voacabar		vocabaris
vocabatur		vocabatur
vocabamur		vocabamini
vocabantur		vocabantur

Vocabantur,	vocabantur,	vocabantur	VOCO!

LANGUAGES III

PROGRESSAURUS' GROUP:

The first two verses of "My Bonnie" in Latin; perhaps with rhythm and instruments.

Trans aequora abiit Chloe;
Abest Chloe longissime:

Trans aequora abiit Chloe;
  Reddatur amata Chloe.
Reddas, reddas, O reddas amatam mihi.

O Zephyre, aequore perfla;
  Oventi, perflate mare;
O Zephyre, aequore perfla;
  Ut mihi reddatur Chloe.

LANGUAGES IV

HISTORY'S GROUP:

(Let yourself go. Look at the first choruses in Names and Nicknames for ideas.)

Grammar!

Bare subject	Bare Predicate	Bare Object
The boy	hit	the boy

Transitional Expressions

Addition:	moreover, further, furthermore, again
Subtraction:	but, yet, nevertheless, still, however
Contrast:	on the other hand, on the one hand, on the contrary
Coincidence:	equally important, meanwhile, in the meantime
	at the same time, at the same place
Purpose:	for this purpose, to this end, with this object
Result:	hence, accordingly, consequently, thus
Summary:	in sum, to sum up, on the whole, in brief

PROGRESSAURUS' GROUP:

Adjectives To Express Yourself With:

maroon	angry	mild	calm
pale	brilliant	bright	sparkling
dark	darkling	belligerent	malevolent
Sylvan	singular	candid	autumnal

HISTORY:

Alfred. Name as many causes of the First World War as you have discovered from your reading in the library.

ALFRED:

Some causes of the First World War are:

ONE	Archduke Ferdinand's Assassination	
TWO	Alsace-Lorraine	
THREE	Militarism	
FOUR	Trade Rivalry	*They march out with reasons still being chanted.*
FIVE	Nationalism	
SIX	Turkey — the Sick Man of Europe	

PROGRESSAURUS:

Now, boys and girls. For this past month we have been living in France.

BRUCE:

Je ne veux pas.

PROGRESSAURUS:

We have cooked French food. *Reaction*. We have talked French. *Reaction*. We have re-enacted many scenes from French history — the triumph of the Romans over the Gauls *SCREAM* St. Bartholemew's Massacre *SCREAM!* — what episode will we re-enact today?

ALL:

The Revolution!

BRUCE:
And Charley, you'll be King Louis Seize.

ALL: *as they crown him*
Louis Seize Louis Seize Louis Seize

> *He is left alone on an improvised throne while the class retreat muttering to one corner.*

Saint Antoine Corvee corvee corvee

Pas de pain pas de pain pas de pain pas de pain

> *Much muttering of these words suddenly boiling over into an attack on some chairs which become the Bastille. Some of the students turn the chairs upside down and whirl them around over their heads.*

Bastille!	Quatorze juillet	quatorze juillet
Aux armes citoyens		ou est le roi
A bas les aristos		Madame la guillotine
Liberte	fraternite	egalite
	Nettoyez les aristos	

> *They seize and lead CHARLEY up the scaffold. He makes gestures.*

"Ma peuple"

> *They murmur.*

Chop!

> *The executioner lifts up a waste paper basket as Louis Seize's head.*

> *CHARLEY rises rather shakily.*

Now, boys and girls, what lesson do we learn from the French Revolution?

174

BEATRICE:

>That democracy doesn't always work too well.

PROGRESSAURUS:

>No, no, no. What do we learn, boys and girls?

ALL:

>Kings are bad, Charley. Democracy is best.

A GEOMETRY LESSON

TERMS AND DEFINITIONS

HISTORY'S GROUP: *this is really a ballet*

Acute angle	axiom	arc of a circle
Hypotenuse	Hypothesis	

Incommensurable magnitudes

Isosceles triangle: a triangle having 2 equal sides

Rhombus   Rhombus   Rhombus   Rhombus:

> a quadrilateral in which the four sides are equal

> Book Three: Proposition Three

To: circumscribe a circle about a triangle

Given: ABC is a triangle

Required: To circumscribe a circle about ABC

Construction   Draw the right bisectors of BC and AC, intersecting at O. Join OA. With centre O and radius OA describe a circle. This circle passes through A, B and C.

Proof: Join OB, OC.

175

O lies on the right bisector of BC,

OB = OC

Similarly   OC = OA

OB = OC = OA

And the circle passes through A, B and C

Question: Is it always possible to circumscibe a circle about a given quadrilateral?

Again, play around with Euclid.

A CHEMISTRY LESSON

PROGRESSAURUS' GROUP:

Coughing as if gas masked, explosives and lightness versus heaviness can be suggested.

Table of the Elements

Hydrogen	Copper
Helium	Zinc
Carbon	Arsenic
Nitrogen	Silver Tin
Oxygen	Antimony
Fluorine	Iodine
Neon	Gold
Sodium	Mercury
Magnesium	Lead
Aluminum	Lead
Silicon	Bismuth
Phosphorus	Radium
Sulphur	Uranium
Chlorine	Americium
Calcium	Curium
Iron	Berkelium
Cobalt	*Californium*
Nickel	Canadium?

DR. PROGRESSAURUS enters with a crutch and a telescope:

PROGRESSAURUS:

Now boys and girls, yesterday we conducted Galileo's experiment at the Leaning Tower of Pisa in which you managed to drop an iron ball on my foot.

BRUCE:

But it fell just as fast as the bale of feathers.

PROGRESSAURUS:

I know. But next time — try to hit my foot with the feathers. Today, following in Galileo's footsteps, how would you like to study the moon through a telescope?

BRUCE: *already looking through*

Charley, there's a strange thing on the moon. I think it's an elephant.

PROGRESSAURUS:

Why so there is. Whatever can be the matter.

They all shade their eyes and stare directly at the moon.

BEATRICE:

I think I've found the difficulty, Dr. Progressaurus. Come and look in this end of the telescope.

PROGRESSAURUS:

Why — someone — somehow a mouse has got down the telescope.

As he reaches in, it climbs up his sleeve and there is a chaotic exodus.

Help! Help!

POETRY

MISS HISTORY'S GROUP:

"The Hummingbird" by Emily Dickinson

A route of evanescence
With a revolving wheel
A resonance of emerald

A rush of cochineal
And every blossom on the bush
Adjusts its tumbled head
The mail from Tunis — probably
An easy morning's ride.

PROGRESSAURUS' GROUP: *a la The Fugs?*

"The Tyger" by William Blake

Tiger, tiger burning bright
In the forests of the night
What immortal hand or eye
Could frame thy fearful symmetry?

In what distant deeps or skies
Burnt the fire of thine eyes
On what wings dare he aspire
What the hand dare seize the fire?

And what shoulder, and what art
Could twist the sinews of thy heart?
And when thy heart began to beat
What dread hand and what dread feet?

What the hammer? What the chain?
In what furnace was thy brain
What the anvil? What dread grasp
Dare its deadly terrors clasp.

When the stars threw down their spears
And watered heaven with their tears
Did he smile his work to see?
Did he who made the Lamb make thee?

Tiger, tiger burning bright
In the forests of the night
What immortal hand or eye
Dare frame thy fearful symmetry.

PROGRESSAURUS:

Very well, boys and girls. You may do what you like until supper time. If any of you want to drive the cars around the race track just feel free to do so. Beatrice, you're very poor at driving. You should get out and practise more.

178

BEATRICE:

I don't want to learn to drive. I might kill somebody, including myself.

PROGRESSAURUS:

Poor Beatrice. YOU'll neve get adjusted to our modern world.

BEATRICE:

I don't want to get adjusted to it. It's 80% hideous.

BRUCE:

Leave her alone, Charley.

> *As DR. PROGRESSAURUS fades away they all wait till he's really gone — then*

O.K. Beatrice. Where are the new lessons?

BEATRICE:

I'm amazed you're anxious to see them, Bruce. Since you can't read them. The cook, Mrs. Smith, was able to get us the whole correspondence lessons for Grade XII Physics. They came in the mail this morning to her from the Department of Education. So *handing out papers* we can get going at studying them.

GIRL:

Has the little chicken who hasn't scratched yet appeared in a dream to you lately, Beatrice?

BEATRICE:

> *She produces the battered Bon Ami can. They all crane forward to look.*

Yes. He appeared last night.

BOY:

Tell us what he told you. Can you?

BEATRICE:

We're soon going to leave this island. On a boat!

ALL:

Leave? On a boat?

BEATRICE:

We're going to be given an examination. It's most important that we do well. And we'll meet another set of young people who've been brought up the way we have.

GIRL:

Will the little chicken still care for us?

BEATRICE:

Of course. He couldn't leave us now. He's all we've got. How could we have lived without him loving us. Let's repeat his worship as we go down to the woods to do our physics problems.

They recite the contents of a Bon Ami can, the French being favoured.

Nettoyez la vaiselle
Nettoyez la vaiselle

Fade off.

MISS HISTORY enters with her group:

HISTORY:

Now — scholars, young men, young women, ladies, gentlemen — this is our farewell dance at the school, for tomorrow we go east on the train to meet your benefactor. In a way you will meet the world for the first time although it also will meet you. Remember that. Now — dance and enjoy yourselves. You have reached the end of what they used to call when I was a girl — Middle School.

They dance — precisely and beautifully.

Switch to a chaotic "Twist" at PROGRESSAURUS' School; then back.

The scene fades and we are ready for THE JUDGMENT.

MR. FROTHINGALE and the GOVERNOR-GENERAL walk along the empty stage as if on a terrace. The GOVERNOR-GENERAL is an incredibly distinguished old man who carries a cane and wears medals.

FROTHINGALE:

Your Excellency, you've no idea how pleased I am that you could come to judge the results of this experiment.

180

GOVERNOR-GENERAL:

But, Frothingale, the pleasure is just about all mine. I too have longed to know which system of education was better. How incredibly enlightened of you to have given two such fanatics as Miss History and Dr. Progressaurus a chance to prove their stuff — ten baby orphans apiece.

FROTHINGALE:

By the way, before they arrive, what method of judgment will you use?

GOVERNOR-GENERAL:

Well, I'll see them as a group at the garden party. But then I would like to have personal interviews. I'll choose the persons completely at random. I should also like some sort of social situation set up. Why not a tea pot with some tea in it and cups and saucers. So often character is revealed in little things like table manners.

Tea table is set up.

Enter HILDA HISTORY and DR. PROGRESSAURUS.

FROTHINGALE:

Why my dear Miss History. And my dear Dr. Progressaurus. How are you after all these years? *Silence.* Goodness gracious. What have I done to you? Have they made you mute?

HISTORY: *laughing*

No indeed, Mr. Frothingale. But it is eighteen years since I've seen you.

FROTHINGALE:

And you, Dr. Progressaurus. Can you still speak to me?

PROGRESSAURUS:

All righty. Golly, I was just waiting for the lady to speak first.

FROTHINGALE:

Well, I can hardly wait to see your products. Miss History's are to come in first. But before that — I must introduce you to His Excellency.

MISS HISTORY curtseys and DR. PROGRESSAURUS bows.

GOVERNOR-GENERAL:

And I am very pleased to meet you. Both of you have given up eighteen years to the worthiest of causes. By the way, before your students enter could you each tell me what you set out to accomplish with your children?

PROGRESSAURUS:

What I tried to do, your Excellency, was to teach the child, not the subject. To teach them to express themselves. They were never forced to do a single thing they didn't want to.

HISTORY:

All I tried to do was give them an education.

GOVERNOR-GENERAL:

I see. Well. Is this your group then, Miss History?

> *MISS HISTORY'S group enters. They are blazered and quiet and neat. The one or two untidy souls are hardly noticeable. HILDA takes over His Excellency and MR. FROTHINGALE to introduce them, as well as PROGRESSAURUS. The scholars bow and curtsey. From the opposite side of the stage come PROGRESSAURUS' GROUP. HILDA'S scholars see them first — REACTION — the grownups turn around and behold them too. All of them are individualists although there are several groups devoted to one brand of individualism. Some lumber, some slouch, some are dressed fit to kill with jewellery. BRUCE'S transistor set blares. One girl twists her drum majorette's baton. The two groups confront each other. There is a silence.*

> *One of MISS HISTORY'S GROUP, a boy, goes over to DR. PROGRESSAURUS and bites his finger — "ouch!"*

BRUCE:

Hey! Lookit, kids. Charley got bitten on the finger by one of them. They'll lose marks for that.

BOY:

Oh I'm awfully sorry, sir. Miss History, I've no conception of why I did that. I apologize abjectly, Dr. Progressaurus. I don't know what got into me. Did I bite you badly?

PROGRESSAURUS:

It's perfectly O.K. Just expressing yourself. Go to it. Here — try the other hand.

HISTORY:

When he was very small, Dr. Progressaurus — you may recall that Baby Number Seven bit you. I think Jerry is Baby Number Seven. This doesn't justify his

182

strange behaviour, of course.

PROGRESSAURUS:

Well — would you say Baby Number Seven has made progress or not, Hilda?

HISTORY:

Yes. With an interesting relapse.

GOVERNOR-GENERAL:

Now, while the rest of you attend Mr. Frothingale's garden party in his large and capacious grounds, I should like to talk to some of you.

Consults a list.

Beatrice and Bruce from this group. And Stephen and Cynthia from this group. One at a time. Cynthia first.

FROTHINGALE:

Let's see which group can run the fastest. Down to the goldfish pond and back.

All disappear save GOVERNOR-GENERAL and CYNTHIA.

GOVERNOR-GENERAL:

Pray be seated, my dear. Do you mind if I ask you a few questions?

CYNTHIA:

No. But do please ask them.

GOVERNOR-GENERAL:

Only a few. That's what I'm here for.

CYNTHIA:

Have you had your tea yet, your Excellency?

GOVERNOR-GENERAL:

No. I haven't.

CYNTHIA:

Perhaps you'd like me to pour it for you then.

GOVERNOR-GENERAL:

Why that would be very pleasant.

CYNTHIA:

And how do you take your tea?

GOVERNOR-GENERAL:

Why, my dear, you've asked me more questions than I have of you.

CYNTHIA:

Only one more.

GOVERNOR-GENERAL:

I take it clear, Cynthia.

She pours him tea.

Cynthia, what's the saddest thing that ever happened to you at Miss History's school?

CYNTHIA:

One of us took ill and died six years ago. We all liked him very much. That was heart-breaking.

GOVERNOR-GENERAL:

Yes. And what was the happiest thing that happened to you at Miss History's school?

CYNTHIA:

When I began to like my music lessons.

GOVERNOR-GENERAL:

You didn't at first?

CYNTHIA:

At first I had temper tantrums, but I got over them. With help. And then suddenly they couldn't get me away from the piano.

GOVERNOR-GENERAL:

Would you like to play for me, Cynthia?

CYNTHIA:

Yes.

She goes to the piano and plays a short piece.

GOVERNOR-GENERAL:

Thank you, Cynthia. You may tell Bruce to come in now.

CYNTHIA curtseys and then retires.

BRUCE: *striding forward*
Hi!

GOVERNOR-GENERAL:
Good-day to you, Bruce. What's that you're listening to?

BRUCE:
Gee. Is that thing on? Music.

Turns off transistor set.

GOVERNOR-GENERAL:
And what are you eating?

BRUCE:
I'm not eating. I'm chewing gum.

GOVERNOR-GENERAL:
I see, Bruce. Who was the first Prime Minister of Canada?

BRUCE:
How would I know? You?

GOVERNOR-GENERAL:
You live in Canada, don't you?

BRUCE:
Do I? I never could figure that out. You know something? It was finally proven to me that I'd been living on an island all these years. Charley made the captain sail the boat all the way around it. Course, it still could have been a trick.

GOVERNOR-GENERAL:
Who is this Charley?

BRUCE:
The guy that teaches us.

GOVERNOR-GENERAL:
Oh. Dr. Progressaurus.

Bruce — I've mislaid my glasses. What does this fine printing say?

BRUCE:

    You got me there, Gov. I can't neither read or write.

GOVERNOR-GENERAL:

    I beg your pardon.

BRUCE:

    Go ahead. Beg it. I'll give it back. You see I never wanted to learn.

GOVERNOR-GENERAL:

    But how on earth did you get into Grade Twelve?

BRUCE:

    Charley always said it'd hurt my feelings if I was failed. So it would have.

        Imitates crying.

    Anyways Beatrice reads the exam questions to me. And my memory's pretty good. Ask me the date of any big battle there's ever been.

GOVERNOR-GENERAL:

    Actium!

BRUCE: *he gives its date*

    You see? These days I figure you don't need to read or write. Just press a button. Know your traffic signals. If you wanna book — get a record.

GOVERNOR-GENERAL:

    Suppose you wanted to write a love letter?

BRUCE:

    Get Beatrice to write it for me. Or send her a tape.

GOVERNOR-GENERAL:

    I see. And are you happy?

BRUCE:

    Happy? Sometimes. Other times. It's that Beatrice. I'd be quite happy chewing gum and listening to my transistor set if she didn't keep saying I was going to turn to stone. I keep feeling my ankles to make sure.

GOVERNOR-GENERAL:

    Well. I guess that's all, Bruce. On your way out could you tell Stephen to come in. Good Heavens! What are you doing?

186

BRUCE balances the tea pot on his head.

BRUCE:

Hey Steve. Come in and see me balance the tea jug.

STEPHEN enters and takes the tea pot off BRUCE'S head.

STEPHEN:

Would you like some more tea, your Excellency?

GOVERNOR-GENERAL:

No. Could I pour you some though?

STEPHEN:

Why yes, that would be very nice. I — I take it clear, sir.

GOVERNOR-GENERAL:

What do you think of Dr. Progressaurus' students?

STEPHEN:

I have an opinion, but I'm keeping it to myself if you don't mind.

GOVERNOR-GENERAL:

By the way, I see my shoe has become untied. Would you mind tying it up for me?

STEPHEN:

I'm sorry, your Excellency, but I always think a man should tie up his own shoes.

GOVERNOR-GENERAL: *at first angry, reaching for his cane, then —*
Why — as a matter of fact it *is* tied. Must be an optical illusion. Do you ever play at Miss History's school? Or do you just work, work, work all the time?

STEPHEN:

Actually we pretty well do what we like. To work is to play.

GOVERNOR-GENERAL:

Ah, you've been brainwashed.

STEPHEN:

Yes. I suppose we have.

GOVERNOR-GENERAL:

What's your favourite pastime?

STEPHEN:

Whist.

GOVERNOR-GENERAL:

Whist?

STEPHEN:

You know — the card game. I could play it day and night. I like mathematics. By the way, could I disagree with you?

GOVERNOR-GENERAL: *stiffly*

Perhaps.

STEPHEN:

When you said we'd been brainwashed at Miss History's class, that's just not so. You have to do something with your mind. It all depends on what *kind* of water you wash it in.

GOVERNOR-GENERAL: *rising in pretended fury*

Do you dare to disagree with the titular ruler of your country?

STEPHEN: *pausing and backing up*

Yes! When it comes to slurring my teacher I'll disagree with anybody.

GOVERNOR-GENERAL: *laughing*

Good, Stephen. You may go now and tell Beatrice to come in.

BEATRICE:

Her clothes are a cross between the wild and the blazer philosophy.

What's been going on in here, your Excellency? I heard raised voices. Oh dear — before I forget *curtseys*

GOVERNOR-GENERAL:

And who taught you to do that?

BEATRICE:

No one really, except I'm as they say, playing this by ear.

GOVERNOR-GENERAL:

Now, Beatrice, what do you think about life in general?

BEATRICE:

Dear me. I didn't know the examination was going to be so tough. Well, here goes.
If it weren't for the little chick who hasn't scratched yet it'd be unbearable.

The GOVERNOR-GENERAL is silent.

BEATRICE:

You look sort of stunned.

GOVERNOR-GENERAL:

I imagine I do. You see most young ladies I know would say — "God" at this point.

BEATRICE:

O.K. God sends the little chicken. Bon Ami. Here he is.

She shows the Bon Ami can.

I found him years ago on a trash heap and then he started to appear to me in dreams.

GOVERNOR-GENERAL:

You've made a whole religion out of an empty can of household cleansing powder?!

BEATRICE:

I guess we have. But we had to do something. You see where it says "good for
cleaning windows" it doesn't just mean windows.

GOVERNOR-GENERAL:

It doesn't?

BEATRICE:

No. It means the windows of the soul. The little chick washes them for you and
hasn't scratched yet.

GOVERNOR-GENERAL:

And do all the rest of you believe in this old tin can?

BEATRICE:

More or less. You see Dr. Progressaurus wouldn't let us believe in him, so.....

GOVERNOR-GENERAL:

Some of you did remarkably well on your Grade Twelve examinations. Wasn't Dr.
Progressaurus responsible for that?

189

BEATRICE:

No. Little Chick was. He appeared to me in a dream and told me to get the cook to send away for the correspondence lessons. Everyone studied hard because they wanted to please the little chick who hasn't scratched yet.

GOVERNOR-GENERAL:

I see. By the way, are all the orphan children who went to Pelee Island with Dr. Progressaurus still in the group?

BEATRICE:

The eagles carried Florrie away.

GOVERNOR-GENERAL:

The eagles carried Florrie away! Good Heavens! What did Dr. Progressaurus do about that?

BEATRICE:

Florrie always had wanted to be an eagle. So he figured it was all right.

GOVERNOR-GENERAL:

Did you ever miss anything on the island?

BEATRICE:

Yes. Someone to rebel against. Charley always gave in too easily.

GOVERNOR-GENERAL:

What do you want the rest of your life to be like?

BEATRICE: *dreamily*

I wrote a poem about it. When I was fourteen. It's a chant poem we all say together. Would you like to hear it?

As she begins the poem her group come in to do it with her and all the others appear also.

Existence gives to me
What does he give to me?

He gives to me: a pebble
He gives to me: a dewdrop
He gives to me: a piece of string
He gives to me: a straw

Pebble dewdrop piece of string straw

190

The pebble is a huge dark hill I must climb
The dewdrop is a great storm lake that we must cross
The string is a road that I cannot find
The straw is a sign whose meaning I forget.

Hill   lake   road   sign

But love and patience do quite change the scene
The desert fades into meadows pleasant and green
The mountain becomes a pebble in my hand
The lake calms down to a dewdrop on a flower
The weary road is a string around your wrist
The mysterious sign is a straw that whistles "Home"

Pebble dewdrop piece of string straw

FROTHINGALE:

Well, your Excellency. Have you made up your mind which school wins?

GOVERNOR-GENERAL:

No, I haven't. I shall just have to walk around a bit till my mind clears.

He walks around — lost for a few moments in the crowd.

A difficult decision. Oh a difficult decision.

HILDA:

My dear. What is that curious bracelet you're wearing?

GIRL:

It's all that's left of my beddie-bye blanket I had when I was a baby. I don't feel secure unless I have it by me.

HISTORY:

Why don't you let me keep it for you? It looks rather — shabby and scruffy, don't you think?

GIRL:

O.K. Gee. Gee, I think I feel much better now.

HISTORY:

Yes. And I'll always keep it for you here. Right in my purse.

GIRLS:

Shame on Bruce. He can't read. He's a non-reading Grade Twelve graduate. Yah, yah, yah Brucie!

BRUCE:

Hilda, your girls are teasing me because I can't read.

GIRLS:

Poor old Bruce. He can't read the street signs.

HISTORY:

The first step, Bruce, is a simple one. What is my name so far as you are concerned?

BRUCE:

Uh — Miss History?

OTHERS:

Beatrice! Look what we found at a store at the bottom of Mr. Frothingale's garden? Twenty cans of Bon Ami cleansing powder with Little Chick's picture on every one of them!

They sprinkle the powder.

GOVERNOR-GENERAL:

It's a tie. By incredible luck for you, Progressaurus, it's a tie. And there's going to be a tie-breaker.

FROTHINGALE:

Oh, how glorious. The experiment can go on. Never fear. Frothingale Breweries made an immense profit last year.

GOVERNOR-GENERAL:

How I propose to break the tie is in the following way: Miss History — Dr. Progressaurus you will exchange your groups for the final year of their high school education.

MISS HISTORY'S GROUP:

No. No.

GOVERNOR-GENERAL:

Miss History — you will go to Pelee Island and what you must do to these poor progressively maladjusted mites is change them without changing what is charming about them — about some of them. Progressaurus, you will go out to the prairies and superintend this group. If you're any good at all they'll have changed you by

192

the time a year is up. Then in a year's time we shall see.

MISS HISTORY faints.

ALL:
It's too much for her. You've killed her. Irregular verbs. Irregular verbs.

GOVERNOR-GENERAL:
No, no, no. She's made of sterner stuff than that. I'd faint myself in her situation. You see, Progressaurus, it's Beatrice who saved your skin and made it a draw.

PROGRESSAURUS:
Beatrice! Why she's my worst student.

GOVERNOR-GENERAL:
No. She's your best. And she could, probably, have flourished only with your kind of neglect.

PROGRESSAURUS:
Stuff and nonsense. Boy, have I got my work cut out for me. Teaching you little snobs to be yourselves.

HISTORY: *rising*
I think that's what made me swoon. The idea that he'd get them. But no — I'm not afraid. You can't make a sow's ear out of a silk purse — even you, Progressaurus, cannot effect *that* miracle. So, yes, I'll let you have my scholars.

BRUCE: *on bended knee*
Oh Miss History — please! Teach me how to read.

Appendix

A Liturgy

Bon Ami
Polishes as it cleans
Makes porcelain gleam
Ne Rougit Pas les Mains

Mode D'Emploi
Directions

No Red Hands
Nettoie les fenetres
N'a pas encore engratigne
Hasn't scratched yet

Polie tout en nettoyant

Use this for the religious scene with the children on the island.